THE BUCKMAN TREATMEN

THE BUCKMAN TREATMENT

or

A Doctor's Detour in North America

by

Dr Rob Buckman

with a lot of support and nagging from
PAUL DUNSTAN
Television Producer & Slavedriver

First published in Great Britain 1989 by
MACMILLAN LONDON LIMITED
4 Little Essex Street London WC2R 3LF
and Basingstoke

Associated companies in Auckland, Delhi, Dublin, Gaborone, Hamburg, Harare, Hong Kong, Johannesburg, Kuala Lumpur, Lagos, Manzini, Melbourne, Mexico City, Nairobi, New York, Singapore and Tokyo.

A CIP catalogue record for this book is available from the British Library.

ISBN 0-333-49813-5

Typeset by Rowland Phototypesetting Limited
Bury St Edmunds, Suffolk.

Printed in Great Britain by
WBC Print Ltd, Bristol

To
My Very Best Friend Ever in the Whole Wide World
Dr Patricia Ann Shaw

CONTENTS

ACKNOWLEDGEMENTS

Some authors' acknowledgements are real, others are a real embarrassment. These ones are real.

I seem to have been involved with the Yorkshire Television Science Office team for a very long time – since I started shaving, perhaps, (1975) and certainly since I stopped (1984). During all that time the head of the office, Duncan Dallas, has been a combination of mentor, father-confessor, tutor and Director of Public Prosecutions. His critical insight and his high standards have kept me humble. Well, *made* me humble actually. Among the higher-ups, John Fairley has always been a keen and receptive supporter of our various efforts – of course, I'd say that even if it wasn't true but in this case fortunately it is. As regards Dunstan – fifty per cent of everything I have said about him is true and neither he nor I know which fifty per cent it is. Paul Bader (widely known by his nickname 'Bader') was the brave and calm man in charge of things in Chicago, and Adam Hart-Davis who, for reasons totally unknown to medical science, is unable to think or talk unless he is wearing a silly hat, ran the show in the Navajo nation.

On the shoots, our gallant cameraman Mostafa Hammuri was always a gentleman and a scholar. This is rare enough anywhere these days, but it is so rare in the world of cameramen that the World Wildlife Fund has declared him an endangered species and he gets regular visits from Princess Anne. He was directed – as were we all – by the unflappable Charlie Flynn whose entire existence has been as an understudy for Kenneth More (with a Scottish accent). We had various odd bods on sound – the oddest was, and is, the extraordinary Lindsay Dodd who firmly believes he is a character in a Rod Steiger movie, although he is not sure which one. Chris Clarkson, on the other hand, believes himself to have been Max Miller in a previous life – there is no other explanation for his behaviour (until the psychiatrist appointed by the court completes his report). Our assistant cameraman during the infamous rattlesnake episode was Dave Barrett who describes himself as 'too numerous to mention' – which can also be said of the several others who assisted us in the many long and desolate hours of any film shoot, i.e. the lunch breaks. The final editing was entrusted to Brian Tomkins who things always in the right order got our schedule shooting film of despite. An easy job not it was.

I am extraordinarily grateful to every member of this gang and shall use this page as my notes for the acceptance speech at the next Oscars (or is it Emmies?) award night if they suddenly decide to create a category for Bizarre Medical Documentaries That Don't Fit Into Any Other Category. We won't get anything for Best Costumes, that's for sure.

And to you, the gallant reader (if you have been). Thank you for reading this, and if you want to buy another copy for a friend who doesn't like reading books, I'll come round and read it to them. Unless I'm in America, of course.

1

INTRODUCTION:

What This Book Is All About

This book is about America – which is a bit of a problem, because I don't know anything about America. But then neither do the Americans. This is because America is not a country at all; it's actually a collection of countries which have very little in common with each other. By which I mean that a Navajo Indian in New Mexico, a Texan oil millionaire and an impoverished snake worshipper in West Virginia are about as typical 'Americans' as a North Sea trawlerman, an Italian film producer and a Bulgarian turnip farmer are typical 'Europeans'.

This makes it a bit difficult for a standard-issue British National Health Service doctor like me to get Out There and explain to you what America is really like. Fortunately, there is an easy way.

The answer lies in Buckman's First Law of Life on Earth, which states that 'Every country gets the health service it deserves'. This means that if you wander around the United States and Canada stopping passers-by and asking a few simple questions about local illnesses, health and life, you get a very accurate and interesting picture of The American Way (which is a phrase the Americans use to mean 'going off in every direction at top speed'). The questions are not very complicated. 'What illnesses do people get around here?', 'What happens to people when they get ill?', 'Where's the local doctor and what does he do?' or 'How do people cope?' will usually give you a good start.

So that is what we did. We wandered about for a couple of years on and off (mostly on, because my hospital wouldn't let me off that much) and filmed what we saw. It was the best and the worst – the best was better than I have seen in Britain, and the worst was worse. But even the average was far from average.

We could only cram about half of our material into the TV series, because there simply wasn't enough time to tell the full stories, so we decided to write The Book of the TV Series. Next year we'll try The T-Shirt of the Book. Then The Cuff-Links of the T-Shirt. And the year after that we'll make The TV Series of the Cuff-Links and begin all over again. It sounds like exploitation and aggressive marketing – but that's The American Way.

If you're sitting comfortably, we'll begin.

2

THE APPALACHIAN MOUNTAINS:

The Docs of Hazard

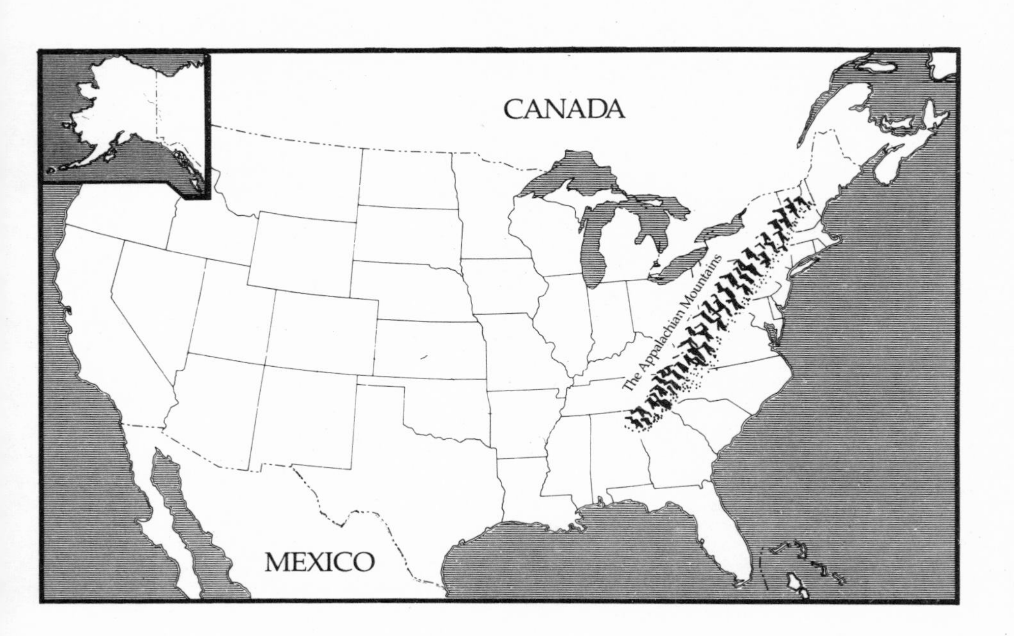

Catfish Man of the Woods:
An Everyday Story of an Appalachian Loony

In America, the system of Free Enterprise prevails, and the concept of freedom is highly prized. In general, the Americans (or most of them) do not feel fettered by many of the social constraints that restrict the behaviour of Europeans. Such as good table manners. Or, occasionally, sanity.

I'm a modest sort of a chap most of the time. Which is only natural, since being a junior doctor in the National Health Service I've got a lot to be modest about. I suppose that boasting is simply not the British medic's style – you don't get signs outside the average NHS hospital saying things like 'ST NISSEN'S HOSPITAL: HOME OF THE WORLD'S FINEST HERNIA REPAIRS' or 'YES! THIS IS THE CLAGSDEN GENERAL – OVER ONE THOUSAND HAEMORRHOIDS REMOVED EACH YEAR!' That's because we British have a rather restrained attitude to our medics and our health. We may sit around talking about our bronchitis and our constipation until our friends' eyeballs have glazed over and several of them have died of sheer boredom, but we don't make a public fuss. But The American Way is not Our Way. Publicly, there don't seem to be the same social (or legal) limitations; and if some doctor or other thinks he can cure the common cold, old age, baldness, impotence, bankruptcy or any other shameful disease of the twentieth century, well he comes right out and says so. Publicly. Just like that.

Now, it so happens that Catfish Man of the Woods is not simply some doctor or other. He is no doctor at all, but he has made it big. No, not just big, I should say Big. In certain parts of the United States he is more famous than any public doctor-figure you can think of – say, Christiaan Barnard (remember him?), Dr David Owen (who?), Dr Spock (oh, *that* Dr Spock) or Dr Crippen (nobody's forgotten him, surely). Catfish Man of the Woods claims he has been on the *Johnny Carson Show*. More than once. Catfish Man of the Woods has letters from patients miraculously cured in thirty-six of the fifty states, and twelve other countries in five continents. Catfish Man of the Woods is clearly a Big Cheese and a Force to be Reckoned With. So no self-respecting visiting doctor (e.g. myself) could set foot in the Appalachian Mountains without visiting Catfish Man of the Woods.

I must admit I did feel like the Town Mouse as I drove my amazingly wonderful power-steered Chevy convertible (hired from the People Who Have to Try Harder) along what was basically a dirt track past Staley's Grocery Store (the last vestige of civilisation for twenty miles) and followed the first of twenty-one unsteadily hand-painted

'CATFISH MAN OF THE WOODS THIS WAY' signs. I wondered about Catfish. Who were his parents – were they a Mr and Mrs Man of the Woods? ('Hi! This is Dogbert Man of the Woods and his wife Nancy Man of the Woods and this is their little boy Catfish'.) No, that didn't sound right – though I later found out that Catfish had a brother who called himself Catfish II (perhaps he had thoughts of marketing his entire life as a movie sequel: *Catfish II – The Brother*). I suppose that Americans have a fairly casual attitude to names and traditions. They just make them up when they need them. And the same applies to reputations – particularly Catfish's.

The trail eventually led to Catfish's surgery. Which was a shack. No, I exaggerate, it was a hovel. I must admit that very few British 'alternative health practitioners' could boast of an office like Catfish's. And the few who had one like it certainly wouldn't boast about it. The best parts were unbelievably tatty; the worst parts were like something out of Tobacco Road. There were more hand-painted signs splattered over the front of the place like an infectious rash: 'BLOW YOUR HORN THREE LONGS AND THREE SHORTS AND I WILL BE WITH YOU IN A FEW MINNITS. I MAY BE AT TOILET. BE PATIENT. REST ROOM AROUND BACK'. I suppose that was the equivalent of the British general practitioner's sign 'Please give your name to the receptionist and be seated in the waiting room'.

Unfortunately, since we were there to make a television programme we didn't have the luxury of waiting even a 'few minnits' so we decided to track him in his lair (and perhaps flush him out; no, perhaps not). The contagion of signs spread round the trunk of the shack and on to the fences at the side, leading to the 'REST ROOM – NO CHILDREN BEYOND THIS POINT'. (What did Catfish do in the Rest Room that children weren't allowed to know about? Or was it that the children of the Appalachian Mountains didn't have bladders or bowels, or perhaps weren't allowed to empty either of them until they became adults?) We made our way to the Rest Room, a solitary privy of the Classic Pioneer style, *circa* 1921. Catfish Man of the Woods was indeed At Toilet, and so I had the extraordinary experience of introducing myself and starting the interview through a convenient knot-hole in the lavatory door. Greater men than me have quailed and turned back at such a prospect, but I am nothing if not brave and persistent.

Being filmed shouting, 'Hello! I'm Robert Buckman from the television company in England. Are you in there, Catfish?' to a lavatory door was unnerving. It was a little bit of the 'I-talk-to-the-trees' kind of lunacy. But fortunately Catfish spends a fair amount of time At Toilet (and when you hear all about his herbal medicine, you'll understand why) and didn't mind in the slightest conducting an interview from the throne.

Catfish Person of the Woods consults his busy appointments schedule in his sumptuous waiting room.

His *spiel* began instantly, and he dashed through a list of the diseases he could cure ('sugardiabetesbloodpressureraisedhivesandshingles tiredbloodbadbackmigraineheadacheperiodcramps', etc., etc.) while still At Toilet, so that the comparison of his words to his actions was rather striking. Eventually Catfish finished his At Toilet, began to be Off Toilet and emerged, still talking at high speed about the diseases he could relieve.

He looked a shambles. His jacket was cut in the style of the more fashionable Idaho potato sacks and had clearly been something of a stranger to the dry cleaners for three or four decades. The only new item of clothing he was wearing was a bright blue West Virginia Locomotive Company peaked cap, obviously a freebie hand-out from a visiting sales rep. Inside the dreadful outfit, Catfish was small, energetic, unshaven, bright-eyed, voluble and bonkers.

He carried on talking as if we'd known each other for years. 'I make the deers run, the rabbits hop and the groundhogs lay down in the shade, and that's what I do for people.' I must admit that I'd always wondered who it was that made the groundhogs lay down in the shade; I thought perhaps it was a federal regulation, but now I knew it was Catfish. Naturally. Then his soliloquy veered off into religion. A lot of it whizzed straight past my ear, but I did catch a fair bit of stuff about things 'that creepeth on the ground' (apart from the groundhogs, I assumed), 'the beasts and the herbs wherein there is life', 'the grass for the cattle and the herbs for the service of man.' At about the fourth minute, Catfish drew his first breath. And so did I. Then he started again.

'Do you realise', he said, not looking at me to find out whether I did realise it or not, whatever it was, 'that if everyone would do what the animals do, and everyone knew what the animals knew, then we'd be knocking people on the head to get rid of 'em, 'cos everyone would be well and there wouldn't be room on earth to walk?' I didn't realise that. On the other hand, I have long suspected that everybody *does* do what the animals do, which is why there *isn't* room on earth to walk. And that is why the world *does* need people to hit other people on the head, as in Central Park, where mugging is clearly a late substitute for birth control. Furthermore I have also suspected that everybody *does* know what the animals know and not much more, which is how the Republicans got in again at the last election. However, since my philosophy was so different from – yet perhaps as bizarre as – Catfish's, I let it pass.

We walked up the hill outside his shack so that he could show me where he gathered the herbs for his patent medicine. He ran up the hillside clutching a trowel and making enthusiastic little dives into the soil like a nervous squirrel in late autumn. The first herb was Sweet Annis. 'What they make liquorice from. It's good for bronchial trouble, sinus trouble, tube trouble, colds and it'll make the fish bite. Put a bit on your fish hook and the fish jumps out of the water and you got him.' Obviously a cure for the once-dreaded epidemic disease of lack-of-fish-biting. Next was Indian Bed-Straw. 'What the Indians used to make their beds from. And they drank it as a tonic too.' Perhaps the more urban descendants of those Indians were even now trying to make a modern herbal remedy of boiled duvets or a tonic from stewed fitted sheets. Who could tell? Then Catfish found some Slippery Elm. The bark of the Slippery Elm, according to Our Man in the Appalachians, 'cures ulcers, haemorrhoids, upset stomach, gas on your stomach, hardening of the arteries, bee stings, snake bites, poison ivy itch, takes corns off your toes, takes calluses off your feet, takes wrinkles off old people's faces, makes girls' skin go tender when they've got rough skin; it's for intercourse lubrication for ladies who've got dry glands and it causes a child to be born one-third easier and for the afterbirth to come by itself without a doctor's help; it's for women to take three weeks before the child is born three times a day, a little piece as big as your fingernail . . .' At that point we were walking up a steep bit of the hill, and I was so busy trying to catch what Catfish was saying that I fell over. 'Does it stop you falling over?' I asked him. For the first time, he was honest. 'No,' he said, but added, 'but if you do fall over, Slippery Elm'll help you get up quicker.' Game, set and match to the loony.

However, the powers of the Slippery Elm were as nought compared to the May Apple. With the May Apple, we are talking Miracle City. 'You take a little bit of May Apple a quarter of an inch long, you got a laxative for the next day.' And, just in case I was volunteering to try it, 'You don't go eating this today 'cos you'll end up going to the rest room and having breakfast all at the same time and you won't have enough toilet paper. And that there May Apple also kills crows, mice, ground squirrels and anything that eats corn in the cornfields.' I wanted to know how the May Apple managed to kill these animals. 'It laxes them to death.' A crow with terminal diarrhoea was a very bad thought indeed, though I seem to have encountered several pigeons with similar problems in Trafalgar Square. Perhaps Catfish was exporting May Apple-flavoured corn to London. Surely not.

By now we had finished the tour of his herb garden and returned to the pharmacy behind his surgery where he prepared his pharmaceutical compounds. It was a dustbin. Catfish tipped an entire bucket of his herbs, together with a fair amount of earth, into the bin, then added a bucketful of water and lit a fire of newspapers and twigs underneath it, compressing the whole mush into the cauldron with a piece of rusting corrugated roof. At least his tonic would give you plenty of iron. I almost felt like writing some more *spiel* for him: 'It's got so much iron, you go to sleep and wake up pointing your feet to magnetic north; it rings the metal detectors at airports, turns you brown in the rain, and if you drink enough of it you can nail yourself down over a hole in your roof and keep your house dry.'

By now he'd wandered back into the surgery, where two customers from out of town were waiting for him. They were both women in their early forties who, it turned out, were divorced, had time on their hands and were quite interested in alternative medicines. Of course, there's alternative and there's Alternative. Catfish was the latter. He grabbed them, diagnosing their complaints instantly as kidney problems. Actually Catfish thought everything was caused by kidney problems, including syphilis. 'People get syphilis who've never been near a woman.' (I didn't know there was anybody who would believe that story these days. Thank goodness for good old Catfish.) 'If your system is bad it'll erupt somewhere in your body and then you gotten syphilis.' Fortunately, although his two customers did have kidney problems, neither of them, according to Dr Man of the Woods, had syphilis. What they both had was excess of water. He showed them where the water came up to in their bodies. It was in the region of the chest, and there was an immense amount of groping as he showed them precisely where their water level was now and where it would go down to when they drank his bitters. Both of them clearly loved being groped by this tiny smelly old man, and they giggled continuously and hugged him back when he hugged them. His success with women made me think I should change my aftershave. To Canal Number Five perhaps.

The finale of our visit was a taste of his fresh-brewed bitters straight from the stewed mess in the dustbin. 'Le Catfish Nouveau 1987. An amusing yet full-bodied bitters, somewhat forward on the palate, an immature nose and a cheeky hint of Sweet Annis and dead crows, contrasting with a firm and bold aftertaste of burnt newspapers and boiled tin. Should be laid down for drinking in ten years, or preferably never.' It tasted exactly as awful as it looked. It was indistinguishable from a specimen of bathwater in which a diabetic horse had recently died. I had no doubt that he could make millions selling the stuff since it tasted so utterly foul that it must be good for you. 'Do you the power of good,' said Catfish. 'In a few minutes it'll go to work and everything that's been bottled up in your head for fifty years will just come pouring out through your nose.' My brains, for instance.

Catfish drained his own cup of bitters to the lees, poured himself a second one and offered us another one. It was clearly time for us to go. Apparently, it was also time for Catfish to go back At Toilet. That was something, at least, that we could believe.

Snake, Rattle & Roll:
The Revivalist Snake-Handlers Go to Church

Many people in what we like to call the 'free world' think of religious tolerance as an absolute requirement of a true democracy, and would regard it as a fundamental rule of any civilised society that nobody should be persecuted simply because of their religious beliefs. And so say all of us, I'm sure. But what happens if the religion involves acts of celebration that are illegal? What would happen if I, say, became inspired tomorrow and founded a church that required all of my church members to spend the whole of Sunday embezzling? Or smashing parking meters (which might make it an immensely popular and well-attended church, now that I think about it)? Or what would happen to me if I was caught burning down somebody's garage and I said that I was simply obeying instructions from my personal God? Perhaps the magistrate might give me a year in the nick and trust that my personal God would visit me regularly and give me strength. Or he might have me assessed by a psychiatrist to ascertain whether or not I was insane. Of course I am expressing the problem in simplistic terms. In practice, individual members of any religious group are not above the laws of the nation simply because they are religious people. Nor do any Judaeo-Christian religions expect that immunity – render unto Caesar those things that are Caesar's, as Jesus said on this very subject. But some religious practices are right on the border of behaviour that the rest of society regards as either criminal or lunatic. And that's where the really tough problems lie. We visited a church of a Christian sect whose religious ceremonies have been outlawed in every single state except this one – West Virginia. The church services involve something a little more drastic than embezzlement or busting parking meters. In fact they consist of a potential (and sometimes actual) form of suicide.

As we drove towards the small town of Jolo the scenery got bleaker and bleaker. It's funny how one's emotional reaction to nature changes when bits of civilisation intrude. Think of a rocky hillside with bits of purple heather and a few short trees on it. What adjectives spring to mind? 'Wild', 'rugged', 'bleak', 'unspoiled' – words that suggest an untamed beauty or similar romantic notion. A good place to go if you're looking for inspiration for your poetry or if your name is Heathcliff and you're being played by Laurence Olivier in the film. But what if there is evidence of human habitation? Think of the same scenery but now add a couple of ramshackle wooden huts with peeling paint hanging off the front doors and cracked window panes, a couple of rusting bicycles and an old tin bath rotting in the yard, plus a car with no wheels resting on bricks, or the skeleton of a broken pram – and now what do you think of? 'Depressed', 'impoverished', 'squalid', 'underprivileged'. The background is the same, but the figures in the foreground make it a different picture.

And that's what we saw as we drove towards Jolo. The scenery changed from unspoiled to spoiled, and then to very spoiled. The first landmarks that showed us that we were getting into spoiled country were the slagheaps. They weren't very big (certainly not by British standards) but they gave the landscape a grey and gloomy tone. As we drove on there seemed to be more and more of them, until they seemed to be the only things for miles around that were flourishing and multiplying. Once upon a time they must have represented the prosperity of the mines, but now they were old and – even for slagheaps – neglected. Further down the road were the ramshackle huts, the beaten-up trailer homes with the peeling paint, the rusted cars on bricks and the rotting prams. And there were occasional people, distinguishable only because they weren't resting on bricks themselves. A few Ancients sat in front of their homes smoking corn-cob pipes. A few children stood around and stared vacantly at the Strangers from Out of Town. This area was clearly the outskirts of Jolo.

Actually it seemed that Jolo consisted of nothing but outskirts. It was a rather scattered sort of mini-town (to call it a village would give the wrong impression), with collections of two or three small houses or trailer homes in dribs and drabs along the road. I suppose that the structure of the typical huddled-together village in Britain evolved that way because everybody wanted to be near the village pump and/or green – or, in more modern times, the pub. But new American small towns evolved after cars were invented and after the roads were built, and were planned with the prevailing American sense of limitless space. As a result their homes seem to do very little in the way of huddling. They are separated and scattered along the road, giving the town a very cold and sparse feeling, like a party at which there aren't enough guests to get it all going. Even in the mid-afternoon sunshine the place felt inhospitable and just a little sinister. I thought of the hillbilly country in *Deliverance* (where Jon Voigt and Burt Reynolds go on a trip and fall foul of some demented toothless inbred maniacal mountain folk). I rather hoped that I would be mistaken for Burt Reynolds (who *wasn't* killed by the natives), though anybody who made that mistake would have to be really demented, if not blind, as well as toothless. In any event, the town seemed to be distinctly lacking in amenities, so it was fairly easy to guess that the locals might be stuck for entertainment of a weekend.

What they actually do is quite peculiar. Each Sunday they go to church and take with them a box of deadly poisonous snakes. They whip themselves up into an evangelical fervour, and when they are at maximum inspiration they release the rattlesnakes and copperheads and dance with them. Quite often they get bitten, sometimes seriously – but it is an absolute rule of the community that if they are bitten they do not seek medical advice, even if this means that they die of the snake bite. Over the years in this area alone, over a dozen people have died of their bites, and what is more they have died in great pain. It sounds like total lunacy, but there is a flimsy theological foundation for their strange habits. In the Gospel According to St Mark there are the following verses:

> And he (Jesus) said unto them, Go ye into all the world and preach the gospel to every creature. He that believeth and is baptised shall be saved: but he that believeth not shall be damned.
>
> And these signs shall follow them that believe: in my name shall they cast out devils: they shall speak with new tongues. They shall take up serpents: and if they drink any deadly thing, it shall not hurt them: they shall lay hands on the sick and they shall recover.

These are the only verses in the New Testament that mention serpents in this context, but the sect of snake-handlers have made it the centre of their doctrine. They do not question the factual and literal meaning of the verses (even though it was much more likely that Jesus was slightly misquoted – since Mark's gospel was written at least forty years after his death – and he was really talking about the inner strength that comes from faith, implying that if you have faith, it doesn't matter what happens to you, you will maintain your integrity and soul). They believe that the Bible must always be taken absolutely literally: although how, for instance, are you meant to render unto Caesar those things that are Caesar's, since there are now no ruling Caesars (unless you count Cesar's Palace in Las Vegas, which would be a very odd place for all Christians to render unto)? Anyway, these verses of St Mark are the literal truth for the worshippers in Jolo, and so each Sunday they dance with their snakes. If that doesn't provide a big enough challenge, they drink strychnine.

Our first appointment was with assistant preacher Dewey Chafin, who doubles as chief snake-catcher and -keeper. His house was small and sparsely furnished – there was a noticeable lack of knick-knacks, personal objects, bits and pieces. Actually his house was so lacking in Things that it looked almost unlived in; I've seen people staying at motels who make their rooms look more homely. There were a couple of devotional pictures on the wall and three bookshelves. Two of the shelves were empty, and the third had seven books – three were copies of the Bible, three were commentaries on the Bible, and one was a novel by Isaac Asimov. Dewey was in his fifties and, at first appearance, he looked sane. He was tall and sandy-haired, with a crinkly country-style face and a warm smile. He would have made a wonderful uncle and an even more wonderful grandfather, particularly if you were interested in poisonous snakes.

We had arrived at feeding time. Dewey took us into the small back room which, curiously, felt more cosy and lived in than the front room. Unlike the rest of the place, this room had lots of Things, but they were all the same. They were cages containing rattlesnakes or copperheads, and I realised that what made the little room feel lived in was the constant shuffle and rattle of the tenants. Dewey respected and loved his snakes. As he moved among the cages, handing out white mice, he looked like any schoolkid with his or her hamsters, or any amateur zoologist with a life's collection of newts or axolotls or whatever. The big difference was that, by and large, schoolkids don't take their pets out at weekends and try to use them as weapons. Anyway, Dewey dished out the white mice (some of which were alive), and the snakes settled down to Sunday lunch. It was very noisy. Snakes don't have very good table manners. I suppose this is because they can't use a knife and fork, since they don't have fingers (or hands or arms, come to that). It means that they have to stop their prey moving (hence the poison fangs) and then eat it in one lump, because they can't cut it up. This may explain why snakes have not invented spaghetti, which would be a particularly awkward food for them. The noise was quite impressive – very much like the sound track of a high-budget horror movie with a prominent *crunch-slurp-gulp* of gristle, blood and bone. Personally I thought it was quite interesting, but our assistant cameraman, Dave, had to leave. He was so frightened of snakes that he had said in advance that if anyone in the crew played any practical jokes he would leave for England straight away. In some respects I could see his point. You know where you are with poisonous snakes, but a film crew can be a much more unpredictable and frightening animal. Anyway, the snakes received their lunch, so that when they took part in the church service they would not be *too* hungry. I mean, the snake-handlers may be slightly loony but they're not totally insane.

We had some time to fill, so Dewey and I sat on the steps of his house and flipped through his family photo album. This was when the whole image of Dewey as a sane family man came unravelled. The album was full of gruesome photographs of church members who had been bitten: people with grotesque swollen faces, bleeding from eyes or nose; people with massive bruises on an arm or leg, with a blackened gangrenous centre or with blood oozing from the puncture.* It was highly unpleasant, but what was even more worrying was the pride that

*Some snake venoms interfere with the ability of blood to clot, so that bleeding from the wound is quite common later.

Dewey Chafin (sponsored for his record-breaking flashy-shirt wearing endeavours by McCann's of Tazewell) flips through his gruesome family album.

Dewey took in the album. It took me a moment to identify what his manner reminded me of. Then I realised – he was like a little child. Do you remember what it was like when you were four or five years old and a friend had a particularly spectacular graze or a really big cut or, even more impressive, needed stitches? Didn't everyone cluster round to have a look, and didn't the patient/hero glow with pride in the scars of battle nobly borne? And haven't we all grown out of it since then? Or if we haven't, don't we try to pretend that we have, and that we're grown-ups now? Well, the snake-handlers of Jolo haven't. All the pride of the kids' playground was alive and well in that album. The worse the bite, the more horrendous the swelling and gangrene, the happier and more smiling the face in the photograph, and the greater the sense of pride with which Dewey showed it to me. As a matter of principle, none of the patients saw physicians; some lost fingers, some lost toes or developed deep scars, and one or two died. So be it. The ones that died, Dewey explained, were those who had the greatest faith. Their deaths were not caused by God as a punishment, but were signs of God trusting them with the greatest test of all.

I had major problems trying to accept this piece of peculiar theology, but I didn't think my concepts of self-inflicted random injury would persuade Dewey to change his views. He showed me a few photos of himself, and tried to look modest as he described being bitten by his snakes *ninety-five times*. The worst one was on the right side of his forehead. The swelling made it impossible for him to open his right eye, and the pain was tremendous. I wondered if he had thought he was going to die; his reply was a little ambiguous. 'I thought it was a possibility, but I never really thought about it.' In any event, he clearly had not been scared of dying, and was now proud of having been tried and tested. It was time for church.

The Church of the Lord Jesus was a plain small building that looked exactly like any of a thousand Boy Scouts' meeting halls anywhere in Britain. Inside, it was remarkable only for the complete absence of any remarkable features whatsoever. At the business end of the hall there was a dais raised a few inches above the floor and a lectern. The end wall was festooned with intimidating notices written in Pentel on odd bits of cardboard: 'NO GOSSIP NO TALEBEARING NO LYING NO BACK-BITING NO BAD LANGUAGE ON THE PULPIT.' I wasn't quite sure if this meant that these activities were permissible elsewhere in the church – an important point since some of the film crew had some important talebearing and backbiting they wanted to get on with. Similarly 'NO MEN WITH LONG HAIR, MUSTACH OR BEARD NO WOMEN CUTTING HAIR OR DRESSES ABOVE KNEES OR SHORT SLEEVES JEWELRY OR MAKEUP ALLOWED ON PULPIT'. I must admit the temptation to cut someone's hair on the pulpit was a strong one, but we all resisted it, particularly those of us with a beard and a 'mustach'.

The preachers in charge were Brother Robert Elkins and his daunting wife Sister Barbara. They seemed a little more peculiar than Dewey, and lacked the sort of bucolic charm and warmth that he had. In his comfortable middle age, Brother Robert was plumpish with greased-back hair, thick glasses and a slightly bureaucratic and distant way of talking. He was the kind of person you might meet in a sub-branch of the Gas Board who tells you firmly and loudly why you can't have whatever it is you want. He took to explaining the relevant verses of St Mark in the same way – the manner that bureaucrats adopt when they're going through the rule book, gaining superiority from their intimate knowledge of the subsections and regulations of which the poor benighted customer is totally ignorant. Brother Robert's wife was bulkier. In the words of the old joke, if I were to try to think of three adjectives to describe Sister Barbara they would be 'very, very strange'. Grey hair piled up, thick glasses and a slight rolling of the gaze made her look like the Headmaster's Wife Who Has Been at the Sherry Again. They introduced me to the church organist, Lydia. Lydia was actually Dewey's niece; her mother (Dewey's sister) had died of a snake bite twenty-five years before. Lydia herself had lost part of a finger to a

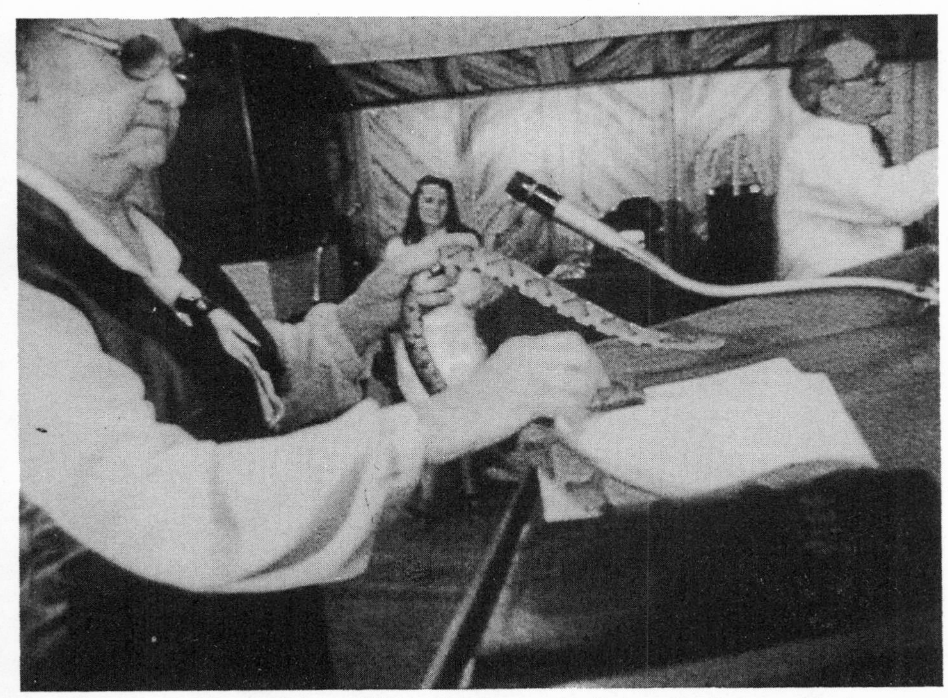

The fearsome Sister Barbara Elkins frightens the living daylights out of an innocent rattlesnake.

snake bite (the photos of her and her gangrenous finger occupied a prominent place in Dewey's album), but that hadn't affected her organ-playing or dimmed her enthusiasm. She, like all the church members, was proud of her experience and had not gone to the doctor's. ('It never entered my head, not one time. The good Lord took me through the pain as well as the prayers of the Saints.')

The congregation of about fifteen adults and four or five children assembled, and the service started up. There was no form of service at all. Brother Robert stood at the pulpit, Lydia sat at the organ, and two guitarists (both superb musicians, as it turned out) sat at the back of the dais; they all waited for inspiration and for the spirit to move them. Sometimes Brother Robert would start an impassioned speech. Sometimes one of the guitarists would start up a strong revivalist-type riff, and everyone would start singing. Sometimes they would do two or three verses of hymns that they knew. Sometimes they would just stand up and dance round. The rhythm and the music were clearly the most important part, and they obviously needed it to get the fervour up. The dancing itself was mostly stomping on the ground or whirling round, often with hands raised in the air – like a hybrid of a hillbilly hootenanny and a religious dervish. After the first half-hour or so, Brother Robert tried to get everyone going with a bit of a rabble-rouser. Holding up the

Dewey-eyed
Dewey Chafin demonstrates his way with our scaly brethren.

Bible, he shouted, 'You know what this is? This is a Road Map to the Kingdom of Heaven! You don't need no other books, you don't need no other learning. This book got everything you need. With this book, you get straight to the Kingdom of Heaven . . .' Things began to warm up. The music started again, and now everybody was on their feet (except the children, who are not allowed to take part in the service and had fallen asleep on the pews). In the middle of the dancing, Dewey unlocked his box of snakes and threw the dozen or so rattlers and copperheads into the middle of the dance floor.

This was the moment. The dancers each grabbed a snake and held it up. One man in his early forties held his snake up at eye height and danced backwards as if hypnotised by his dancing partner. An older lady just picked one up for a few moments and then put it down. Dewey was totally involved with his and draped it around him like (is this the real origin of the word?) a feather-boa. As with Dewey's photo album, there was a sense of childishness about it – the dancers were daring the snakes to bite them, and showing off how brave and unafraid they were. But at the same time they were involved in a religious ceremony. It was a mass exercise in a game of Russian roulette blessed by God. The dancers offered their faces and arms to the snakes, but there were no takers. Whether the snakes had had one too many white mice for lunch, or whether they simply found the worshippers too unattractive as a source of fast food, I cannot say. All that is certain is that nobody got bitten, and after twenty minutes or so Dewey locked them back into their box. The congregation tried to look unmoved as the snakes went home, but I detected a slight measure of relief.

After the snakes, the strychnine. Fearsome Sister Barbara had mixed the solution of strychnine herself. ('I just let the Lord guide my hand. He tells me how much to put in.' Obviously this particular version of the Lord would not make a very trustworthy pharmacist – or chef, come to that.) Sister Barbara pulled out the jam jar with the strychnine and had a swig. Her face was exactly like that of a mother swallowing a teaspoon of penicillin to show her child that it's not that bad really. (The face that says, 'See, *I* can do it, so why can't you?' even though the child knows that firstly Mummy doesn't have to take the whole dose, and secondly Mummy is probably going to spit it out as soon as she's out of sight.) Brother Robert took a swig too, and had the same face. ('See! Nothing to it!') Neither of them died. The evening was running down. There had been no major injuries and no major dramas. I did not really know whether this meant that the evening was a success or a failure, and whether the participants were triumphant or disappointed. Brother Robert made a few valedictory remarks, and the congregation simmered down, woke up their children and filed out into the night. There would be no more excitement in Jolo until next Sunday.

Postscript

You will have gathered that I was disturbed by what I saw in Jolo. I am always disturbed by mass hysteria, even if it only involves a dozen people and does no harm at all. I am disturbed because it reminds me of how weak and gullible we all are. That particular part of the Appalachians was impoverished and deprived. The local people had nothing much to do in the evenings except watch television, so that the fervour and the excitement of their zoological Russian roulette were the bright spots of the week. It's understandable. But this is not simply a pastime to fill in the odd weekend when there's nothing better to do. They have consciously rejected the outside world and feel strongly that *only* they have the One True Road Map to the Kingdom of Heaven. That kind of religious arrogance worries me deeply and puts me off. When any religious group claim strongly that God is speaking to them exclusively, I know that it's time for me to go home. If I can find the One True Road Map.

3

LOUISIANA:

Underneath the Arches

A Farewell to Armadillos: I Help the Doctor Do Some Research into Leprosy

Louisiana is a wonderful and strange place. There is a greater sense of history and of the past here than in most states of the USA. The medical problems of Louisiana are also rooted in the past, and among the most striking is the problem of leprosy. Leprosy, now called Hansen's disease to reduce the social stigma, is still a small but significant problem here, and the largest treatment and research centre in America is situated near Baton Rouge. The research programme there is world class, but it uses some unorthodox methodology that produces a genuinely American combination of high technology and true grit.

I didn't know that leprosy still existed in the United States. I had assumed that it was prevalent only in Africa and Asia and was exclusively a problem of underdeveloped countries. It came as a surprise to find that some areas of the States are, medically speaking, *that* underdeveloped. In fact, there are about 6,000 people with Hansen's disease (the Bible would have called them 'lepers', but nobody would do so nowadays) living in the USA now.* Of those, about 350 patients are looked after at the Hansen's Disease Research Center near Baton Rouge. We went there to meet Dr Richard Truman, a physician who has made research into and the treatment of leprosy his life's work.

The large colonial-style white buildings of the research centre looked like something out of *Gone with the Wind*. The elegant colonnades, long windows and spacious verandas made me long to sit in a rocking chair and sip a mint julep – and that is saying a lot, since I have no idea what a mint julep is, or tastes like. The campus has an elegant and welcoming air, very far removed from the images conjured up by the word 'leprarium'. We checked in and went to meet Dr Truman. Now, the only previous Hansen's disease specialist that I had ever heard of was Dr Albert Schweitzer, whose picture I remembered from my *Children's Encyclopaedia*. Dr Schweitzer was a silver-haired, kindly, god-like figure, redolent of compassion and saintliness. Dr Richard Truman was no ancient Schweitzer; in fact, he looked like a younger version of Pat Boone. He was young and clean-cut, and he looked as fresh as a daisy in his neatly pressed white outfit. No less compassionate and caring than a Schweitzer, he was also bright and witty. He told me of some of the advantages of specialising in Hansen's disease: 'It's a great line to tell people at parties. You get to be first in line for the cheese dip.'

Richard showed me round the large hospital. Funnily enough, once

*The total number of people with Hansen's disease in the world is currently estimated at between 10 million and 14 million.

you are in a hospital corridor, it could be anywhere in the world. Most hospital corridors are damp and approximately eight miles long. And by an unwritten and secret regulation recognised all over the world, they are all painted the same colour, a peculiar kind of depressing off-cream which is unavailable for any other purpose and cannot be found on any other walls.

As we walked along, Richard explained that, contrary to popular belief, leprosy is not very contagious. Ninety-five per cent of the world's population is actually immune to it and could not catch it even if exposed to millions of the germs. The other five per cent are at risk, since, for unknown reasons, they lack the natural immunity of the rest of the population. Even so, that five per cent of the population would have to get a very heavy exposure to the germs to catch the disease. I wanted to know why, if this was true, lepers were excluded from society in biblical times and in later centuries had to ring bells as they approached communities. Richard told me that many of the so-called lepers of biblical times probably didn't have leprosy at all; most of them probably had syphilis. The reputation of leprosy, even in the present era, as a rapidly contagious disease is totally false.

The lack of infectiousness is in fact one of the main problems with leprosy research. Because it is so difficult to transmit the condition from one person to another, it is extremely difficult to study the disease and thus help the five per cent of the population who are at risk. For decades it was thought that human beings were the only animal species that could harbour the leprosy bacterium, and therefore that research on the transmission of the disease would be difficult, if not impossible, because of the slowness of transmission. Then, by a stroke of serendipity that marks most human research, some genius found that there was another animal that carried the leprosy bacterium and, without developing the disease itself, passed the bacterium on to its contacts. That animal was, unexpectedly, the armadillo. Researchers found that there are just under half a million infected armadillos in Louisiana alone, and that each armadillo carries about one thousand billion (in other words, a trillion) bacteria. This means that, in theory, one armadillo could infect about eighty-four humans – although, as Richard pointed out, they would have to live together for a very long time. At present, the armadillos are the main source of the bacteria for the medical research at the centre, and they will be even more important if there is to be a vaccine in the future.

The main thrust of current research is to track the armadillos and find out how they transmit the bacteria from one to another, and how long they have to spend in contact with each other to do so. This requires a type of field research rarely practised by doctors. Basically, every few weeks, they all go on an armadillo hunt. They try to locate the female armadillos and put radio collars on them so that they can track their movements. The next armadillo hunt was that night, and Richard graciously invited me to join. Unblooded as I am in any hunting sport, I was keen to find out what it was like.

The raiding party assembled that evening down by the levee. I must admit that I didn't know what a levee was until Don Maclean's song 'The Day the Music Died' brought the word to British attention (*'Bye Bye, Miss American Pie / Took my Chevy to the levee / But the levee was dry'*). I was then informed that a levee is the bank of a river in the South – a bit like a dyke. And that is where we congregated. Richard had now changed out of his white ducks into combat gear and was joined in a pick-up truck by a motley crew of zoologists who were clearly experienced in the hunting of the armadillo. The whole thing looked a bit like a pretend war, and as we set off I kept on thinking of the adventure as an Ernest Hemingway short story. Throughout the long evening, Hemingway's short sentences full of machismo and bravery kept on running through my mind.

Actually it was quite wet and cold in the back of the jeep as we started the hunt – or, as Hemingway might have put it:

> *There were six of us in the raiding party. Truman said it would be a good raid and we would make many captures. Truman and Benson were in the cab of the jeep where it was warm and dry. We were in the back of the jeep which was open and which was not warm and dry. We drove towards the levee and it began to rain. We began to become cold and wet. Except Truman and Benson, who stayed warm and dry. It was dusk. The sun was setting. Truman said the sun often set at dusk and we all nodded. Truman was the wisest of us all. Truman was a doctor. The rest of us were not doctors. Except me. I was a doctor too. But I didn't know as much as Truman. Truman knew about our mission. Tonight, Truman said, we would hunt only females. We would make many captures, but we would let the males go. We would keep only the females. I asked Truman if this was because we were all males. Truman said that I should not talk like an idiot, I was a doctor. And so was he. And we were all scientists. Our interest in the females was purely scientific. So we must be very quiet as we bounced down along the levee at dusk. If we were very quiet we would capture many females.*

As we bounced along, I noticed that thick thunder clouds were gathering in the sky. To be honest, I don't mind thunderstorms, but I prefer to watch them from a snuggly bed somewhere. Of course, it would never have been macho to admit a fear of thunder and lightning:

> *We were all holding long poles with nets on the end to make our captures with. When the thunder clouds hid the sun, Kitson and Schwartz said they were glad they were not holding long poles made of copper in case there was lightning.*
>
> *Kitson's pole was made of wood. Schwartz's pole was also made of wood. The Radio Man's pole was also made of wood. My pole was made of copper. I said I*

would like to swap poles with either Kitson or Schwartz. Kitson and Schwartz pretended not to hear me and talked about the ball game last night.

It did not thunder and there was no lightning. I was glad. But there was rain. It fell on us. It made us wet. It did not fall on Truman or Benson, who were still inside the jeep in the dry and the warm. The sun set and it was dark on the levee. Truman said it was often dark when the sun set because there are no lights on the levee. Truman said the natives call this time of day 'night' and we all nodded. Benson turned on the big searchlight at the front of the jeep and we all began to look for females.

Actually, our first sighting of our prey came quite quickly.

Benson shouted that he had seen one. He pointed the big searchlight at it. It was moving quite fast. It was an armadillo. This was good because we were hunting for armadillos. We were hunting for female armadillos but from a distance of three hundred feet you cannot tell whether an armadillo is male or female. Maybe even armadillos cannot tell from a distance of three hundred feet. So they often get closer to each other before they try to do the mating thing which armadillos enjoy. We enjoy the mating thing too. Particularly with females. But not with female armadillos. We were hunting female armadillos to put radios on them. We would listen to the radios and we would know where the female armadillos were. Truman said this was important. I asked Truman if we wanted to know where the females were so that we could sell the information to the male armadillos. Truman told me to stop talking like an idiot.

Doing what comes naturally
The armadillo defends itself by a primitive but effective means against the Great White Hunters (note the Great Wet Trousers).

Then came the moment of truth:

We saw the armadillo running. It was two feet long and light brown and covered in armour. It had a long nose, but a longer tail. It was running in a very funny way. It was not running at all, but bouncing. It bounced up and down. After it bounced up, it bounced down. Truman said this is because of gravity. You cannot bounce up and then bounce up again, you have to bounce down first. We all nodded. The armadillo looked very funny. I started to laugh. Kitson and Schwartz and the Radio Man did not laugh because they had seen armadillos often before. They did not think they were funny any more. I looked at the armadillo bouncing up and down and I laughed more. Then we all had to jump out of the jeep. I jumped out and I fell and I twisted my ankle. This helped me to stop laughing. We ran down the bank of the levee, which was wet and slippery. Truman stayed behind in the warm. Truman was the smartest of all of us. He was a doctor. I was a doctor too, but now I was running down the slippery bank of the levee trying to catch a bouncing armadillo with my long net. I was not very good. I am not good with things made with poles and nets. I am not good at fishing. I am not good at lacrosse or tennis. I am not good at golf. I am very bad at hunting the armadillo. I tried to use my net but I missed because when I made the net come down, the armadillo bounced up. Also I started laughing again. Schwartz did better. He caught the armadillo. The Radio Man came to look. It was not a female armadillo. It was a male armadillo. I do not know much about armadillos, but I am a doctor and it was not difficult to see that this armadillo was male. I came closer to look at the armadillo's maleness. As I came closer the armadillo did the thing that male armadillos do when they are not pleased with their situation. It made urine. The urine went on my trousers. This made me laugh. It also made Kitson and Schwartz laugh. It also made the Radio Man laugh and there are not many things that make a Radio Man laugh. Though somebody else getting their trousers urinated on is one of them.

We let the male armadillo go and it ran away, bouncing. Or perhaps it bounced away, running. Who can tell? We got back on the jeep and drove on. Benson used the big searchlight to the left and to the right. Soon we found another armadillo. It was bouncing, too. Kitson said this is because bouncing is what armadillos do best. Apart from wetting people's trousers when they are not pleased with their situation. This armadillo was doing the bouncing thing and doing it well. We jumped out of the jeep again, and this time I did not twist my ankle. But as we ran down the levee, I did a different thing. I fell over. I got up and chased the armadillo with my pole and net. This time I brought the net down over the armadillo. I had caught the armadillo and the Radio Man said I could hold it while he looked at it. It was very big. Because it was covered in armour it was very heavy. It was much heavier than I thought. Also it was difficult to hold if you were worried about your trousers getting wet again. I was worried about my trousers getting wet again. But this time the armadillo was a female. So it did a different thing. And its different things went on my shoes. This made the Radio Man laugh even more. But Kitson and Schwartz said it was a female and this was good. So the Radio Man took one of his radios and taped it around the neck of the female armadillo. Then he tuned his receiver so he could hear the noise the radio made. He said it was just fine. So we let the female armadillo go and the Radio Man followed it with his receiver. Truman said we would come back tomorrow and see how far the female armadillo had gone.

Gotcha!
Two fully grown males (human) demonstrate that together they can just about overpower one young female (armadillan). All's fair in love and war.

For tonight we had done well. I had captured a female. I had done well. Now I could go home and dry my trousers. And clean my shoes. It had been a good hunt. It had not been a clean hunt, but often hunting is not clean. That is what scientific research is all about, said Truman. We all nodded. Truman is a doctor.

The hunt – despite the fun – had been a small part of a major research effort into a disfiguring and potentially curable disease. I hope that the future brings Richard Truman some success with his research. After all, Truman is a doctor.

Doing Right Bayou: I Meet the Strange and Gentle People of the Swamps

Less than an hour's drive from New Orleans takes you into an area of beautiful creeks and swamps which are known as bayou, chiefly inhabited by a people called the Cajuns. My own sense of history and geography was a little vague – I rather thought that the Bayou were the medieval people who wove their history into the famous Bayou Tapestry and I was vaguely expecting Cajuns to be some form of descendant of the Injuns. In fact, bayou country is a remarkable region, much of it untouched by twentieth-century America. And the local people are trying to keep it that way.

Highway I-10 symbolises the attitude of the United States to bayou country. It goes straight over it, without allowing the traveller to see it or slow down for it. In fact, the federal government literally overlooked the Cajuns for centuries until it needed conscripts for the Second World War. The Cajuns are descendants of a religious splinter group who originally lived in Canada. As Catholics they refused to swear allegiance to the English throne and were persecuted. A few of them migrated south to Louisiana and became known as Acadians (Acadia was the region of their origin), a name which degenerated into its present form, Cajuns. From about 1740 onwards the Cajuns settled in the area and kept themselves to themselves. They spoke their native French, and until recently many of them couldn't speak English at all. They lived in the bayou, fishing, growing food and avoiding sending their children to government schools or paying taxes. If there is such a thing as the good life in the States, theirs must have been a close approximation to it.

Then the government found out about them while carrying out a census of everybody who might be suitable for the army. They were

Underneath the arches
America drives past overhead on Interstate Highway I-11 while Greg Guirard takes me by the scenic route on Local Byway and Backwater Atchafalaya A-1.

registered for voting and conscription, and their children learned to speak English – well, American, anyway. The government built a huge highway through bayou country over the creeks and rivers on top of vast colonnades, and while America drives along over the bayou at 70 m.p.h. in trucks and Chevies, underneath the arches Cajun life goes on in motor boats at 20 m.p.h.

The correct name of the area is the Atchafalaya Basin. I believe that the Atchafalaya is the only river in the world to be named after a sneeze but I could be wrong. We started with a general tour, our guide being the incredibly laid-back Greg Guirard. He looked a bit like Kris Kristofferson, with the very handsome slightly wrinkled face and cool eyes which women call 'dashingly handsome' (the same women would probably have called me 'dashingly ugly', but never mind). Greg was a true man of the swamps, spending most of his time scudding about the creeks and rivers in his motor boat and often photographing the bayou in their early-morning glory or evening peace. He seemed to know every inch of the territory and every inhabitant. As we passed by, the locals would all shout a greeting from their boats. At least, I assumed it was a greeting – the dialect and accent made it unintelligible to me; but they were smiling, so if in reality they were cursing him they must have been extremely fine actors. The area was incredibly beautiful.

Branching off the wide Atchafalaya River, which is the water equivalent of the I-10, every little bayou had something new to offer. Most were overgrown with long colonnades of trees meeting overhead in a friendly living thatch, and filtering the light to a dramatic dapple. In some, the water was completely covered with a thick layer of water lilies through which the boat seemed to inch forward in silence like a child on an expensive carpet. The most mysterious area of all was an abandoned cypress grove. The cypress had been cut down in the nineteenth century for the settlers' homes, and the water level had since risen, giving the grove of stumps rising from the swamp an eerie, graveyard look. Greg loved being in the bayou more than an olive loves being in a Martini, and I could see why. Our only culture gap was in the humour department. I asked him if he'd heard tell of my cousin, the local equivalent of Crocodile Dundee, who went by the name of Alligator Ginsberg. Greg said he hadn't, but would be sure to let me know if he did. You can't win 'em all.

Sadly, Dunstan and I had to stop being tourists and get on with our job, which was to find out something about the health of the local inhabitants. Now, I should point out that although the bayou are the most prominent geographical feature of the region, most of the Cajuns live in real towns on dry land and drive cars on roads (in order to get to their boats). We sought out the chief pharmacist, Sid Dupois (a French name meaning Sid O'Peas). Sid's shop was in St Martinville, near other local establishments including Le Petit Paris Ecole de Danse and Theriot's Drygoods and Tackle. This was very France, particularly for America.

Sid was very worried about the Cajuns' health. For all their laid-back, *laissez-faire* attitude, the Cajuns have a most unhealthy diet. Many decades ago, they incorporated into their cooking some of the dietary flavouring of the local black Creole people, heavy users of spices and cayenne pepper. But despite the international reputation of Creole cooking, and the fame of 'blackened catfish' and other Creole dishes, what most Cajuns *really* eat for most of the time is deep-fat-fried stodge. Chips and red meat make up a major part of the diet, and when they indulge in potentially healthier foods such as crawfish (a local staple) they usually deep-fry them first. Only the famous gumbo (which is a thick rich spicy seafood soup) can be called healthy. In addition, the Cajuns take little exercise other than the traditional Saturday-night dance which is usually a wonderful country-style thrash. As a result of this lifestyle, one of the most popular hobbies for Cajun men is having heart attacks, and their average life span is noticeably shorter than the average for the rest of the States. A merry life, but a short one. After some deliberation, Dunstan and I decided it would not be rewarding to try to interview people who had actually died of their lifestyle, but that it would probably be better to talk to the people who were surviving and flourishing. (Dunstan and I can sort this kind of thing out in a trice when we've a mind to.)

We returned to the bayou to look for the survivor types. Perhaps the best example of a true-grit survivor was Carline Berard, and, ironically, she had ended up living on the bayou by accident. In her twenties she had married a man who was a committed bayou dweller. With some hesitation and trepidation, Carline agreed to move out to the bayou with him, and they settled on a small peninsula. Despite being within a few miles of New Orleans, it was as far from civilisation as one could imagine. The only access to their plot of land was by boat. To approach it by land you would have to hack your way through dense undergrowth and lush forest-style vegetation; you could just about do it if you happened to have two squadrons of Marines with you, but it would take a year. There was no piped water, no sewers, electricity, phones, mail, dustbin collection, lamp-posts, hamburger joints, neighbours, muggers, beggars, insurance salesmen, Jehovah's Witnesses, double-glazing salesmen or any other of the amenities and perils that go with city life. There was just the river, the rain, the pets and the land. Carline and her husband settled in much as the Pilgrim Fathers did, cleared a plot of the land, planted vegetables, collected rainwater, lived off their fishing and occasional forays into town for things that don't grow (such as soap and baked beans) and led what sounds like an idyllic existence. And then, quite suddenly and unexpectedly, at the tragically young age of forty-two, he died. Carline, who had moved into the bayou somewhat unwillingly to start with, could easily have left and gone back to her familiar city life, as her parents wanted her to do. But she decided to stay on, and at the time we visited her she had been living there for ten years, four of them alone after her husband's death.

As it turned out, our job in finding her was not that easy. It wasn't exactly a case of Number 23 Railway Cuttings, Cheam ('third turning on the left after the cinema, ah here's No. 21, must be this one next door, etc.'). It was actually a case of 'third bend in the river after the bit where it flattens out after the bit where it gets narrow, then look for two planks masquerading as a jetty, and when you get to a place where there are two branches directly opposite each other you'll know you've gone too far'. Despite the usual inability of Dunstan and myself to map-read our way out of a toilet, we actually managed moderately well while being slightly English about the unusual voyage. If we weren't exactly imitations of Sanders of the River, we were nearly George Sanders of the River, which was almost as good.

We located Carline's landing-stage/plank and scrambled ashore up the mud bank. Dense trees and bushes came right to the top of the bank, and once we were on to her plot of land, we might just as well have been in an Amazonian rain forest. No, I take that back, since I've no idea what

In an Atchafalaya country garden
Carline Berard and I admire the fertile garden with its flourishing zucchini, anthills, and rainwater buckets.

an Amazonian rain forest looks like. This was like a hothouse in Kew Gardens. Only one word sprang to mind – 'lush'. Carline took us on a tour of the house and vegetable garden. The house itself was small and sparsely furnished but very attractive. In terms of amenities it was primitive – every drop of rainwater was collected and used for washing (fortunately there seemed to be a lot of it). I naturally assumed that rainwater, since it had this tendency to fall directly from the sky, would be pure and drinkable, but Carline didn't touch the stuff. She was so worried about pollution of the atmosphere causing acid rain that she got her drinking water from her parents' house (which received the city's purified water) whenever she visited them. This was a fascinating example of American technology reducing a natural resource to the point where people had to rely on American technology instead of the natural resource. The house was neat and tidy, faintly reminiscent of a sixties flower-person's retirement home. There were many books, and a guitar which provided Carline with her evening's entertainment.

If the house was a model of restraint, the garden was a model of nature in full throttle. You could almost hear the plants growing. It was the kind of garden where you could throw a broomstick down and the thing would grow. The atmosphere was moist and heavy, and the soil underfoot was ditto, with tidy rows of huge green things of many different shapes. Carline showed me huge tomatoes, cucumbers and zucchini – in fact, it was a mixed salad in kit form. There were several things which I didn't recognise but I was sure I *could* have recognised them if they were cut up and covered in vinaigrette dressing. Other life forms flourished as well, as I found out when I inadvertently stepped backwards into an anthill and a skirmishing party of ten million fat brown ants came out to indicate that they did not wish to be disturbed by the media.

Carline and I went fishing together. Or rather, we cruised the lines she had set the day before. We hauled in a fairly large fish which I instantly recognised as a fairly large fish. It flopped about in the way that fishes do, so Carline killed it and gutted it, which stopped it flopping about. Carline's world was far from the frantic dog-eat-dog race of commercial America; this was the leisurely human-eat-fish race, and it worked. Her attitude to civilisation (or the nearest equivalent) had also changed over the years. 'At first I seemed to be scared of everything, then I got used to it. Now I wouldn't live anywhere else. Sometimes I can get lonely, but then I can get lonely in a town. I don't think loneliness is where you are at. It's a state of mind.'

Carline seemed to be the archetypal survivor. She was compactly built, with a look of wiry strength and resilience to her. She radiated enviable health. She expressed her philosophy on health quite simply: 'If I get sick, I just go to bed, drink plenty of water and let my body heal itself. And if I can't get out, then here's as good a place as any to die.' Although I am a great lover of my creature comforts (and anybody else's if I can get them), as we said goodbye to Carline I did feel a little envy of the way she had become so adapted to her lifestyle and so comfortable in her surroundings. Perhaps it doesn't matter where you decide to live, as long as you live in a place that you like so much you wouldn't mind dying there. Which, in a way, is a great compliment to the bayou – and to Carline.

Our next visit was to the neighbourhood professional elder, a wonderful and wiry old bird called Alcide Verret. Alcide was perpetually busy ('I don't stop moving. Exercise don't kill nobody, I guarantee you that. My neighbours and friends died younger than me because they took life too easy'). And his own example was a fairly compelling one; Alcide had made it to eight-seven years old, with no sign of fading out. As we clambered ashore in the early-afternoon sun, Alcide told us he'd been busy all day cooking and gardening. I had no difficulty believing him. The garden was neatly tended but jam-packed. Everywhere you looked there were little shrubs, trees and gadgets, all in perfect working order and all obviously requiring care and attention and the kind of exercise that don't kill nobody. Alcide's garden had a few pests, mind you, but nothing simple like greenfly or blackfly. It was the armadillos. I wasn't sure whether Alcide had to get out around the garden flitting DDT into the shrubbery and knocking the pesky armadillos out of the trees, but I didn't want to appear ignorant so I didn't ask him.

I was, however, quite taken with his solar panels that he had installed to give him electricity. Alcide was taken with them too, and he proudly explained that it wasn't cheating, because it comes from the sun and the moon and the stars. 'I get twelve and a half amps from the sun, and five and a half amps from the moon and the stars,' he said – which seemed a neat explanation of the physical universe as we know it. I'm sure if anyone ever gets around to asking God why He put the moon and the stars up there in the firmament, He'll just come right out and say: 'To give Alcide Verret his five and a half amps, of course.' Actually, the Divine Architect had been good in many ways to Alcide, and Alcide had been quick to use what he'd been given. He exercised all the skills he could; besides his abilities in the garden and his domestic engineering and plumbing, he was also a superb cook and enjoyed local fame for his lavish dinner parties. Of course, I enjoy cooking too, but there are only two dishes that I can cook really well (cheese sandwiches and Nesquik), whereas Alcide can do almost anything. We tasted his renowned 'upside-down pudding', which had pears, peaches, bits of syrupy

Alcide Verret and the author sit on the porch enjoying the sun and its twelve-and-a-half amps.

sweet things and delicious fruit juices, and was extremely wonderful. While we were doing the dishes (Alcide has running water and a toilet, which are both regarded as frivolous luxuries by other Basin people), Alcide said that he could cook anything you can put in a pot. 'I never cooked anything where I didn't win a blue ribbon.' I believed him.

Alcide, like Carline, had a fairly relaxed attitude to health. He goes to see his doctor regularly twice a year for a 'physical' and last needed medical attention for an illness eighteen years ago. In fact, his doctor can't find anything wrong with him and has decided that there must be something out there in the Atchafalaya Basin that preserves life. So now Alcide's doctor wants to retire out there and find the elixir of life the Atchafalaya brings to its inhabitants.

Alcide, too, was a survivor. He had come through more personal tragedies than any other three people and yet remained not only stoical but also optimistic. His first wife and their two children were killed in 1929 when a storekeeper sold her gasoline instead of kerosene for their stove. His second wife died of a rare medical condition, and when his third fiancée died of a heart attack before they could get married Alcide 'decided the good Lord wanted me to stay by myself'. Which he had.

A lot of Alcide's philosophy and approach to health was perfectly correct. He ate well, took lots of (home-grown) vegetables in his diet, exercised regularly and steadily and took good care of himself. But perhaps the one factor he played down was the most important: his genes. Alcide's family members were all long-lived; he had an aunt of 102 – which reminds me of one of my old consultant's favourite aphorisms: 'If you wish to live a long time, then you must select your parents with great care.' It's advice Alcide had clearly taken to heart.

After our visits to two lone survivors our final call that day was to a survivor couple, Harold and Myrtle Bigler. In the same way in which Alcide's intricate and busy garden was the incarnation of his lifestyle, the Biglers' house was the allegory of their life. It had been moved five times and been blown apart by a tornado but was still standing in roughly the same place, only looking a bit lopsided. Harold had married an older woman. Myrtle was eighty-seven, and the blushing groom she had snatched from the cradle was a mere seventy-seven and sprightly with it. Their house was set back from the river and was (when we arrived) about twelve feet above the water level. This, it seemed, was a fairly flexible state of affairs. Floods and tornadoes seemed to be a recurrent problem in this particular area of the Atchafalaya (perhaps the equivalent of the wrong side of the tracks), and the Biglers had got used to finding the river calling on them if they were too busy to visit it. Floods up to doorstep level were so common one hardly spoke of them, and floods up to window level were a fact of life. So why didn't Harold and Myrtle move house? Well, actually they had moved house five

Bigler and Bigler
Harold and Myrtle try to relax while wondering why I seem to have six fingers on my left hand.

times but not quite in the way in which you and I understand it. When we move house, we sell the house to someone else (which can be difficult if said house is under four feet of water, but with a clever estate agent you can make anything sound good) and we buy another house and move into it. The Biglers didn't do it that way. They stayed in the house and moved it. Apparently, this is a well-known local habit. Men come round with a big crane and a whole load of thick rollers. They push the rollers under the house and then pull the whole bang-shoot a few yards away with the crane. Of course, the house doesn't like it, not after the first three or four times anyway, and eventually it gets to be a bit weak in the spine. Which is why, after the fifth move, when a tornado had struck five years before, the house had developed a permanent and very picturesque list to starboard of about thirty degrees. Not surprisingly, the Biglers didn't spend too much time sitting at home (probably too dangerous) but spent most of every day on the bayou, returning only for the evening meal and a night's kip.

We sat on the rickety porch as the sun set. The Biglers had a wonderful style of talking – halfway between a double act and an argument. They seemed to know each other's timing perfectly and despite the veneer of bickering had a deep sense of affection and caring for each other. They spoke about the future and how they would try to look after each other as they became less and less able to cope with the physical demands of bayou life. Harold had had the most recent brush with illness, a hernia. He had been to see a doctor who had asked him how he had let himself get into that shape. Harold didn't know what shape he was in. The doctor had declared him unfit for backwoods life and had asked him when he had last sought medical advice. Harold thought it was in the army forty years before. So the doctor patched up Harold's hernia and declared him in good enough shape to get back into the backwoods for another forty years.

And so – I hope – they were, both of them. Battered but unbowed, stoical but still spry and humorous, the Biglers were clearly leading a good life. Doing right by each other, and right by their environment – doing right bayou.

Postscript

As I have said several times, I'm a townie. It's not that I love or need the grime and clamour of a city, it's just that I've never lived anywhere else and don't know of any other lifestyle. When I stay at a friend's in the country, far from the roar of early-morning North London traffic, I wake up suddenly at 6.30 a.m. shrieking, 'What wasn't that?' But I really liked the bayou, and the bayou people. Life there (apart from the deep-fat-fried stodge) was so un-hysterical, so un-frantic, so un-American. Greg, Carline, Alcide and the Biglers all seemed to have made some pact of peace with their environment – something I would see later in Arizona, but which is generally something of a rarity. I loved what little I saw of the bayou and rather envied the locals their peaceful co-existence with their surroundings, and the assurance they all showed in knowing what they really wanted out of life.

4
MINNESOTA:
Winter and the Fourth of July

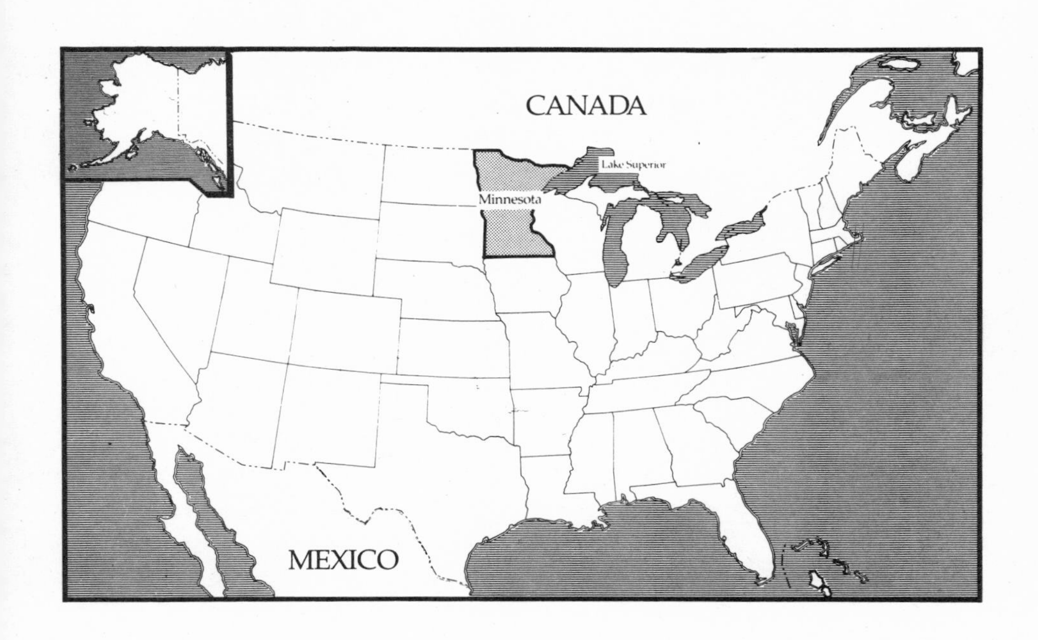

In It Up to My Neck: Bob Pozos Saves Me from Death by Freezing. Eventually

In America, the past isn't what it used to be. Mind you, there are those who say it never was. In any event, in the bad old days long gone, the early version of the average American was a hardy pioneer battling nature and the elements (including the indigenous Indians) and suffering the extremes of heat and cold, flood and famine, plague and pestilence, Abbott and Costello and so on. Nowadays, because the pioneering has all been done, the American doesn't need to be hardy, so he or she has become foolhardy instead. Whereas in the past people would freeze to death in the Klondike or die in the Arizonan desert trying to scratch a living, nowadays they are just as likely to meet death and danger on their holidays. They bake to death on a joy ride because their recreational vehicle runs out of fuel; they freeze when they fall out of their yachts on Lake Superior or when their snow-skidoos go through the ice on the rivers. As an American, if you don't have constant danger threatening your livelihood as your ancestors did, you can at least look for it in your leisure. Which means that somebody has got to try to save the leisured Americans from themselves. One of the very best people working on that problem is Bob Pozos, who tries to help his fellow Americans survive the bitter cold of the Minnesota winters.

It was all Dunstan's fault. He thought it would be 'exciting', and in some respects he was right. After all, it was probably very 'exciting' to watch somebody being guillotined. However – and I don't wish to quibble – it might not have been so 'exciting' if you were the somebody who was actually being guillotined. In any event, Dunstan had heard about this amazing scientist who did research experiments on volunteers in order to design suits that would prevent death by freezing, and now nothing would do except my volunteering. I was given to understand that volunteering actually meant being immersed in freezing water with heart monitoring and temperature probes in unaccustomed parts of the body, while the scientists watched and recorded because it was 'exciting'. It certainly was – in retrospect.

The University of Minnesota science building was very plush and rather grand in a glitzy sort of way. It had the kind of noise-absorbent carpeting that covers all the floors and crawls up the walls so that everyone and everything is quiet as if surrounded by a rich and reverential sound-swallowing atmosphere. A sort of hushed plush perhaps. I have often wondered whether our British universities have such a hard time because we haven't got enough carpeting. Perhaps it's the quiet and reverential carpets that get the American researchers going. Or perhaps it's why they need so many multi-million-dollar grants.

However, the plush carpets stopped at Bob Pozos's door. His laboratory was somewhat more utilitarian. It was carpeted in a material which looked like concrete and which, on closer inspection, turned out to be concrete. On the other hand, he did have his own swimming pool. In the middle of the laboratory there was a shortish pool standing up ten feet from the floor with windows in the side so that the scientists could watch the swimmers. As we came in, a volunteer student was in the pool, hanging on to a steel bar across it and watching television. It could have been a scene of rare domestic bliss except for the fact that every few minutes Bob Pozos and his assistants tipped ten pounds of ice into the pool, which was by then about three degrees above freezing. The team were watching through the little glass windows in the side of the pool, which made the scene exactly like Hugh Hefner's Playboy mansion, except that the student was a male and not a Playmate of the Month. He wore a not-at-all-revealing swimming costume, a whole leash of complicated wiring disappeared into his trunks, and he was freezing to death. My first impression was that he seemed fairly happy bobbing in among the ice like a twist of lemon in a gin and tonic. My second impression was that he must have been out of his mind or being paid a fortune. My third impression was that if I offered to double his fee perhaps he would stay there and substitute for me, especially since he was clearly very good at freezing to death. However, his turn came to an end; Bob Pozos hauled him out, congratulated him and extracted the leash of wires from the poor chap's downbelows.

Bob Pozos is one of those Americans who know what they are doing, and know that they know what they are doing. He was very relaxed, witty, articulate and good company. In short, he was not the sort of man one would expect to earn his living from sadistic acts like causing people to drown and freeze. Even so, he clearly enjoyed his work, and it crossed my mind that many articulate, smiling and pleasant human beings later turn out to have curious quirks to their personalities – like spending their weekends biting the heads off dogs. In fact, Bob was not like that at all. He was genuinely motivated by his desire to save life. He explained to me that Lake Superior is a very large body of water and takes an unconscionably long time to warm up. In fact, it never does, and even in the height of summer it never gets warmer than fifty degrees Fahrenheit. Although that may not sound too bad to you as you sit comfortably reading this, when one actually experiences it, one's first thought is '***', meaning 'If I was a packet of frozen peas I could be stored safely for three months at this temperature.' However, most people who are unfortunate enough to fall into Lake Superior are not packets of frozen peas and, sadly, they would survive only forty minutes. This seemed (to the next volunteer-victim) to be quite a long time. In particular, I remembered reading in *Gorky Park* how if a man fell into the water in Siberia and then stood up in the wind, he would die in less than thirty seconds. Bob said this was total nonsense, which I found very reassuring although I had decided to cancel my planned swimming tour of Siberia anyway. Bob himself came from a much warmer climate, but was attracted to the cold of Minnesota because there was simply so much of it – a grandiose excess. 'We are the Texans of cold,' he put it, and even as an Englishman I had to agree with him.

Bob and I were getting along famously and having a really nice chat when Dunstan came trotting up and ruined it all by insisting that I change into my swimming trunks and get into the pool. Dunstan has learned over the years that when I am very frightened or under great physical duress the result is what he calls 'good television'. Dunstan claims that he, like Bob, is not actually a sadist but is simply motivated by the higher objectives of life on earth such as making good television programmes (a contradiction in terms if ever I knew of one). I incline to the opposite interpretation and believe that Dunstan is, in fact, a practising sadist. I have since been informed by a reliable source that at weekends, although Dunstan never bites little dogs, he does spend hours tearing the wings off flies and designing chlorine-biphenyl nerve gases for use on elementary schoolchildren and kindly silver-haired old ladies. However, since Bob had been kind enough to offer the use of his swimming pool (and temperature probes), this was clearly not the right time to attempt a psychoanalytic examination of Dunstan's personality defects. So I got changed.

Hot air rises. Cold air sinks. This means that when you are poised over a swimming pool which is at four degrees centigrade, you have very little idea of how cold the water actually is. When, subsequently, you enter the water you have very little idea of anything else. I got in quickly, and immediately my brain went into overload. Emergency signals came flooding in from all areas of my periphery into the 'fight-or-flight' centres of my brain and they all strongly recommended 'flight'. Now. Every part of my body was telling me that the struggle to stay alive was unequal and that they (my various parts) had unilaterally decided to give up and would now develop frostbite, go black and drop off. Fear and pain coalesced in my mind into one simple crystalline concept. Since the cameras were running I couldn't say it. But I thought it, repeatedly like an expletive mantra.

Some people have said that extreme cold doesn't really cause pain, and they were right. It was a sensation considerably worse than pain. In pain you know that one bit of you hurts and that all the other bits of you don't hurt (unless all of them do, in which case you don't). With extreme cold, the feeling was of something worse than mere pain – it was a

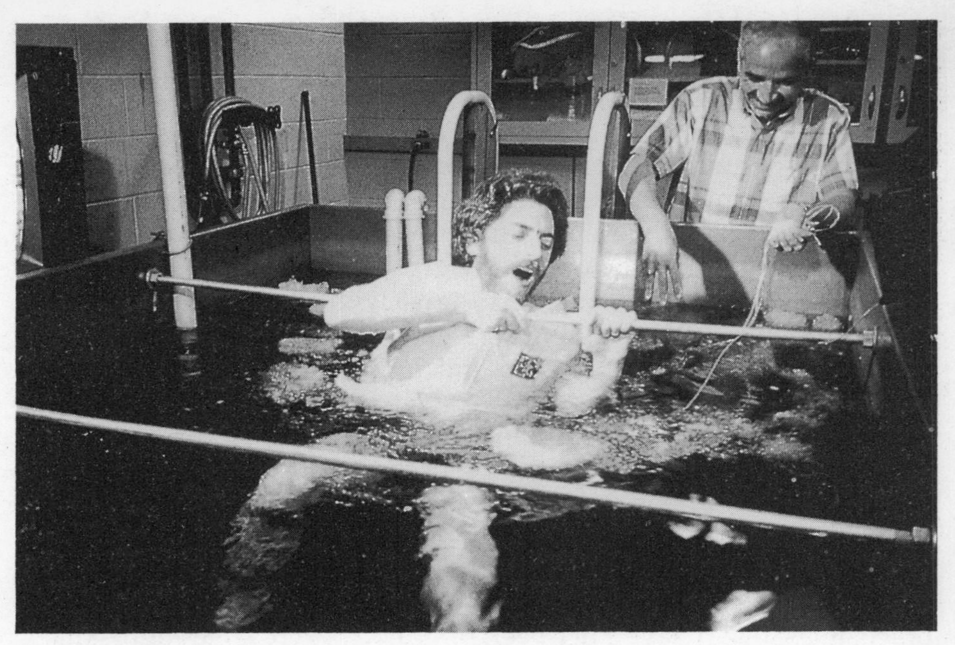

Frozen waists
I suffer immeasurably below the Plimsoll line.

feeling of imminent dissolution, of very near death, of turning into a gelid icicle of frozen protoplasm. I seemed to have nerve endings everywhere, even in my socks, which developed the nylon equivalent of gangrene. But then the intensity faded. I can't say that things became easier, but it was as if somebody cut off your right leg with a rusty bayonet and then started cutting off your left one with a clean bayonet. It was more of the same, but it wasn't really worse. My screaming decreased. So Bob tipped a new load of ice into the pool, and the intensity returned. I thought of England and public schools and how generations of Englishmen had had their young personalities beaten into shape with cold showers and the cane. Suddenly it explained a lot. I could see why the Victorians would want to conquer and subjugate all of India, Africa, Australia and any other place in the world where there were no cold showers.

Eventually, when the temperature probes (which I could no longer feel, along with the area in which they resided) registered 'nearly dead', Bob Pozos pulled me out. And then he took me to the cold room. The cold room is maintained at thirty degrees fahrenheit WITH FANS BLOWING COLD AIR AT HIGH VELOCITY THROUGH IT. You may not believe me, but the proverb 'out of the frying pan into the fire' sprang to mind. Except that at that particular instant I would have

Not drowning but waving
I demonstrate my ability to keep afloat while looking like Andy Pandy after his operation.

welcomed any variation on frying pans, fires, toasters or even school dinners. But these were not on my list of options. What I had was this Force Nine blizzard blowing over all of my shivering wizened little frame. As the new level of cold pain bit into me I suddenly missed the freezing swimming pool. It was an odd feeling, but at least in the pool I had had the cold water surrounding me – which, by comparison with what I was now going through, felt distinctly cosy. Then I remembered my previous discussion with Bob. What was happening to me now was the same as happened to the people in Siberia in *Gorky Park*. What would happen if Bob was wrong and people *did* die in thirty seconds? And if so, how many seconds had I had so far? Because, if I was going to die in a few seconds I certainly didn't want to waste my last few seconds of life wondering how many of my last few seconds of life I'd wasted wondering how many of my last few seconds of life I'd wasted. I mean, it would seem so silly.

This time they were recording my heartbeat and rhythm while the television crew watched (outside in the tropical warmth previously known as 'room temperature') and they were able to inform me unequivocally (through the thick door) that I was still alive and doing fine. I wondered how the word 'fine' was being defined, and by whom. It was quite, quite horrible. My muscles went into spasms, and I did a fair approximation of someone who has been poisoned by strychnine. I tried to keep my mind occupied with cheerful thoughts, but the only ones that came to mind were that if I died I would like to come back to earth as an ice lolly and haunt Dunstan by slipping down his neck in winter. By now my ECG trace (which is the thing in the doctor programmes that goes *phneep-phnerr-blipp* when the patient is alive and *mneeeee* when the patient isn't) was clearly getting ready to go *mneeeee*. In my mind I saw the *Star Trek*-type display flashing 'LIFE FUNCTIONS TERMINATED'. Of course, by Dunstan's reckoning, that would have made *very* good television. Just as I got ready to breathe my last, they pulled me out of the room. Well, they said I was still perfectly safe, but I think they were just trying to play down the danger. I was so cold that when half my chest-hairs came off with the ECG leads I didn't feel a thing. My brain was receiving no messages whatsoever from any distant part of my body. I had to get Dunstan to give a visual check-up on the number, position and colour of fingers, toes and other Outlying Areas. He said all were present and correct, and I have never trusted him less.

However, this was only a rehearsal – an undress rehearsal perhaps, but certainly not the real thing. The real thing came the next day when Bob took us out into the middle of Lake Superior on a coastguard patrol boat to test the amazing new survival suit. The suit itself was a bit like an Andy Pandy outfit for a giant. It was a huge padded red thing with zips and pockets and hoods and stuff. I was absolutely convinced that it would save me from death by freezing. But I was also convinced that it was so unmanoeuvrable and clumsy that I would become tangled up in it and die of panic. I clambered into the suit and had the odd sensation of taking a step and finding that I was moving inside the suit, which followed me rather grudgingly. I poised myself on the edge of the boat, certain that in a few seconds I would be immersed, flooded and drowned. However, nobody likes to appear a coward in front of a film crew, so I smiled bravely. By this stage I was so deep inside the suit that they couldn't see or hear me anyway, so I just went back to cursing them all with my expletive mantra. As in a dream I heard Bob shout 'Now!' in the distance, and I leaped. I don't even remember hitting the water. The next instant I was comfortably on my back, cosy and warm, bobbing up and down like an android marker buoy. It was lovely. I paddled myself around so I could see the boat and waved (which was actually easier in the water than on board). After a few minutes of my scudding about and making noises like Ratty and Mole, I was pulled in. I had survived Lake Superior. Bob Pozos was clearly a Superior scientist, and I had never been more grateful for any man's skills.

Barking up the Wrong Tree?: Mark Tucker Reconstructs His Life

For a health-conscious nation, the Americans have a large collection of phrases that mean insane or crazy. Some of them are quite colourful (such as 'off his trolley', 'out to lunch', 'out in left field', 'a basket case'). When I visited Mark Tucker in the Biggest Treehouse in the World I was reminded of another phrase meaning bonkers. It was 'out of his tree'. Mark wasn't actually crazy, but he was being driven very hard by something. And whatever it was had started by driving him Into His Tree.

St Louis Park is the kind of Good Neighborhood suburb that every American would like to live in (except the kind of people who would hate to live in that kind of suburb). Rows of neat and tidy hedges neatly divide the neat and tidy gardens from the equally neat and tidy gardens next door. Nice. Dull. Lovely place to live, but I wouldn't particularly want to visit there, as they say. But then there is this house on the corner. It is also neat and tidy and also has a neat and tidy hedge, but it is

Room at the top

slightly different. Mainly because it is the only house on the street with a six-storey treehouse rising sixty feet above ground level. Mind you, it is also the only house in the *world* with a sixty-foot treehouse, so I suppose the rest of the houses on the block need not have felt too badly about it.

It doesn't matter what kind of cynic you are, the sheer size and look of the Biggest Treehouse in the World are real magic. There it is, at the end of the garden path in an ordinary garden, the treehouse of every child's dreams – sturdy, intricate, massive and alluring. Of course, I am basically a cool, calm and predominantly objective and rational doctor. So when I looked at this childhood dream made reality, I remember saying in a calm and rational doctorly way: 'OH WOW OH IT'S GREAT OH WOW I WANT TO CLIMB IN THE TREEHOUSE OH WOW, etc., etc.' Which I then did.

I started to climb the first flight of wooden steps, and the real fun began. The whole point of a really good treehouse (and I speak as a child who never had one, and who never knew anybody who had one) is that it should be high up, and once inside it you should be able to be completely hidden from the grown-ups. Mark's treehouse was as intricate and secret as a Chinese box puzzle, with little verandas, tiny rooms, sudden trapdoors, ladders, stairways, peepholes and windows. All of these took you not only *up*, but *into* the tree, so that you felt more and more enclosed and cosy. The higher I got, the more my mental age fell. By the time I reached the fourth storey I was nine years old. I think I expressed my mixture of emotions very well when I said (under my breath), 'Ohboyohboyohboy.' (I tend to get a little repetitive when I'm having fun.)

Mark Tucker was at the top, on the sixth deck, preparing for construction of the seventh. I expected that he would be someone who would really understand the dreams of childhood – and the principles of good carpentry. Mark clearly had both qualities. However, his story was not an easy one, and the wonderful treehouse was actually born out of pain, bewilderment, guilt and doubt.

Mark and his wife Cathi had been doing very nicely thank you. By the early 1980s his career in the insurance business was 'going gangbusters' (an American phrase which means 'doing very nicely thank you'). They had bought the house in the neat and tidy neighbourhood, had had five neat and tidy children, and then somehow the centre of everything went missing. Mark described how his job and business worries took over and left him no time and energy for his family (not a rare problem in America – or anywhere else, come to that). There didn't seem to be time for anything other than grumbling about how little time there was for anything. Cathi and he seemed to be growing apart, and Mark had no time or energy for the children. The symbol of his negligence was the treehouse he never built for his son, Ross. For twelve years he had promised Ross that he would build him a treehouse, and it never happened. For some husbands, the task is different (with me, it was usually putting up the shelves in the spare room), but for the Tuckers the big silver maple tree in the garden was a constant reminder that Daddy wasn't doing his Daddying properly.

The marriage staggered on for a time, but eventually Mark and Cathi came to a parting of the ways. As he told me about it, Mark was (appropriately) sparing of the details, but it was clearly a very sad and disappointing time, and I suspect that Mark went through a period of deep despair and self-doubt. But, as sometimes happens, the misery gave him the impetus to look for a real answer to his life's crisis. He started a major rethink. As a result of it, he went through a psychological and spiritual renaissance. He found God and, more important, found that religion was something that he and Cathi could share. From that foundation, they started all over again. They were remarried, and Mark moved back in. I had the strong impression that, as he started his marriage again, Mark was full of new resolutions and was subconsciously looking for a symbol of the rebuilding of his life. The one that seemed appropriate was the treehouse that for twelve years he had continuously and meticulously not built. Mark told me that the idea of building the treehouse was a truly divine mission and came from God – though I pointed out that God's previous instructions about trees to Adam and Eve had generally been to stay away from them rather than to build houses in them.

In any event, Mark's mission seemed to come at a time of great need. At that particular point, Ross – the son who had been promised the treehouse – had left home and had gone to live with his grandmother. Mark took this as a deep and personal criticism. A black mark for Mark, as it were. So he bought some planks and nails and, never having done any major carpentry (apart from the shelves in the spare room), he started with a single platform on the lowest branch of the tree.

It's difficult to decide at what point the hobby turned into an obsession, and a healthy bit of postponed Daddying came to the verge of unhealthy monomania. Mark was quite sure that when he began he had no intention of building the Biggest Treehouse in the World. But, like Topsy, it just growed and growed. He found new skills and new strength as the work progressed. As an impressed observer, I must say that Mark's workmanship was wonderful; the treehouse was built to last, and was finished with the kind of care and attention to detail which, for centuries, everybody has said died out centuries ago. Each time Mark topped off a storey he thought the treehouse was finished, but then he saw that another storey might just fit nicely into that branch up there. And there might just be room for a little balcony here, with perhaps another little cubby-hole there and so on.

His son came back – initially, to visit and to watch Dad build the treehouse, but then to stay and to live. And Mark worked on. By now, he was doing less and less of the insurance stuff and more and more of the treehouse stuff. In fact, he was working an eighteen-hour day and he remembers on one occasion his work was interrupted by the police, who asked him to give it a rest. He wanted to know why he should stop, whereupon they pointed out to him that it was three o'clock in the morning and his neighbours were going crazy with the hammering and sawing.

As the treehouse grew, it took up more and more of Mark's life. He ran a phone line in from the house so he could handle his business from what he now calls his 'branch office'. There is room for bunks for the children, and he has designed spaces for a fridge freezer, microwave and video recorder – all the essentials of twentieth-century American life, even in a tree. All over his office are motivational slogans encouraging him to think large (they've worked), mingled, in The American Way, with biblical quotations and maxims. We moved up to the top deck, and Mark looked wistfully up at the next set of branches, which could obviously support another storey. I asked him whether he would ever stop building the house. 'Yes', he replied, but I'm not sure that either of us believed it.

He said half-seriously that it was taking him closer to God. I reminded him of the Tower of Babel. He pointed out that his particular tower was taking him *into* nature (i.e. the tree), not away from it. But he was aware that he hadn't quite answered the point.

I liked Mark very much. He seemed to be an intelligent, thoughtful and energetic man who sincerely wanted to do the right thing for himself and his family. But on the debit side, he seemed to have a problem controlling his obsessional drives. In a socially acceptable and thoroughly American Grand Style, he was turning all his psychological turmoil into frantic (but elegant) construction work. And, in America, that turns you into a star or at least a celebrity, which then hides from you and everybody else the fact that what you are doing isn't good for your mental health.

Mark's was certainly the most beautiful treehouse in the world. But even so, isn't a person who spends 92 per cent of his mental and physical energy in his tree actually 'out of his tree'? It's true that Mark didn't *look* like the typical obsessive hobbyist one sees in Britain – the people who build ten-foot-high models of Chartres Cathedral out of milk-bottle tops, or a perfect replica of the Great Western Railway system and recreate the 1921 timetable every Tuesday. He didn't have a manic gleam in his eye and he didn't foam at the mouth. But there was a certain desperate quality to his intensity. The treehouse was visible, well founded, solid, close to nature and growing upwards from firm foundations. He wanted his life to be the same, but it wasn't. I had the impression that his treehouse was overshadowing the rest of his life, in the same way his insurance business had done previously. There was a certain symbolism in the way the treehouse was twenty feet taller than his home. It overshadowed it. It was larger than life.

We didn't talk to Cathi (she wouldn't let us); I think the publicity and the attention rather frightened her and kept her away. Perhaps the fanfares and the all-American hero-worship of Mark had made it even more difficult for her to be heard in the marriage. As we left, I remember hoping that the treehouse wasn't bringing an unwelcome spotlight on to the Tucker family. I hoped it wasn't an apparent cure that made the disease worse. Let's hope my worries are unnecessary. If tree therapy works for the Tucker marriage, then it will be a form of psychotherapy with the best spin-off imaginable. After all, many of us can build castles in the air, but only a few of us get to live in them.

5

LOS ANGELES:

A Long Way from the Angels

The Real Ee-Aw Men: Santa Ana Fire to the Rescue

I never knew that I was an ee-aw man until one Sunday afternoon in the Casualty Department of St Nissen's in 1973, where I met Brian, a six-year-old with suspected appendicitis. I was a junior doctor, and Brian explained to me that I was an ee-aw man because people came to hospital to see me in ambulances that went past his house with their sirens on going 'ee-aw-ee-aw-ee-aw'. I must say that for the rest of that day I felt a special pride in my exalted status, though it has faded somewhat since. In truth, I am not and have never been a REAL ee-aw man, but in the district of Santa Ana, one of the less salubrious suburbs of Los Angeles, I met some true-life ee-aw men – the paramedics of the local fire brigade – who are as close to real-life heroes as one will ever see.

Fascination with fire engines is a universal attribute of mankind. In fact, some psychologists have shown that the desire to watch a fire engine and see where it is going is the third most powerful motive force in human beings – closely following the two most basic primeval urges, hunger and sex, and occasionally getting into first place if a fire engine goes past just after lunch or whatever. But seriously, there is something universally compelling in the way the uniformed men of the fire brigade dash through the streets on their gleaming machines, ignoring traffic lights and breaking all the rules that we lesser mortals are bound by. Best of all, they are on their way to do noble and heroic deeds of selfless courage. Their lives are the answer to all of our rescue fantasies and our fascination with authority. In many parts of the United States, the fire brigades are so efficient at getting to any part of their territory quickly that they have also become an essential part of the health services. Local authorities graft medical services on to the Fire Department's delivery system by creating a specialised hybrid of a fireman and a medical attendant called a paramedic. Usually, the paramedics start out as firemen;* and having trained as firemen they then go through a fairly extensive medical course that qualifies them to cope with most medical emergencies.

But their day-to-day life is under the jurisdiction of the Fire Department, so that they spend their working hours in a fire station and do all the normal things that firemen do, e.g. polishing the big gleaming fire engine, cleaning their boots, watching TV and trying to be relaxed, knowing that any second they are likely to be called out to ee-aw somewhere or other.

*In other districts, some paramedics start out as ambulance attendants – a pattern that is being explored in some areas of Britain now.

We arrived at Santa Ana #3 District Fire Station in the middle of the morning shift on a fairly quiet day. My head was full of intelligent questions to ask about the life of a paramedic. But the Number Three Primeval Urge took over as soon as we pulled into the yard and saw the huge gleaming 1961 Crown firetruck twinkling in the sunlight like a fairground Wurlitzer. The film crew and I were all the same – a squadron of hardened and seasoned professional news-gatherers, lining up alongside the flanks of the shiny beast like a gaggle of kindergarten kids with their fingers in their mouths going coo-er-look-at-that-scuse-me-mister-what-does-that-bit-do-wow, etc.

In my childhood I stood and coo-er'ed alongside many beautiful British fire engines. (Most of them had the name Dennis in chrome on the front. I once asked a fireman why all the brigades called their engines the same name and wouldn't they rather call some of them Freddy the Fire Engine or even Robert after me, one of their most devoted fans?) So I hope I don't seem unfaithful when I say that the American version was somehow showier and in every way brassier. Of course, their country is a lot bigger than ours, which means that the roads are bigger and wider, which in turn means that the fire engines can be built bigger and can still get in and out without blocking the whole street. But even so, this was a magnificent beast. It was about twenty-four feet long, with a huge friendly bull-nose look to its front end, and it seemed to have about four hundred little platforms and cubby-holes where the firemen sat or stored their gear. Everywhere you looked there were twinkling brass hand-rails, twinkling brass knobs or twinkling brass taps. And there were ten big dials telling the firemen all manner of important things about the water tanks and pressure. These were *real* dials – not the kind of namby-pamby designer-dials you get as cars' speedometers nowadays, with amber faces and grey designer lettering, but huge dials with real thick glass over the front, big black metal pointers and numbers printed in big black enamel letters on a heavy-looking white enamel dial face. They were the kind of dial you would expect in a good old RAF Spitfire or a Royal Navy submarine, probably hand-painted by the plucky wives of Our Boys in Blue doing their bit for the free world; dials that spoke of the time when men were heroes and their lives depended on nothing but sheer guts and huge dials, in the golden age before all of this modern lily-livered computer and remote-control stuff, yessiree.

Personally, I would have been quite happy to spend the rest of the day round the old firetruck. I was certain that I could think of many intelligent questions to ask the paramedics about the machine (e.g. ''Scuse me, mister, what does this bit do?'). But just as we were getting really interested, the Red Phone rang. Somebody, somewhere wanted the ee-aw men right away.

I was secretly hoping that getting the crew out of the station would have a touch of RAF style – firm and loud (but calm) cries of 'Scramble, Number Two Squadron' or 'Chocks away, Tiger. This one's yours' – but it was actually a bit more polite. Sadly, we weren't allowed on the actual firetruck (the Number Three Ambition, closely allied to the Number Three Primeval Urge, to ride a real fire engine, would have to remain unfulfilled). Instead we had to follow in the highly specialised paramedic ambulance which was really almost as good. We had three seconds to meet the two paramedics Chris Harris and Chris McKernan, who would be pilot and co-pilot, and the medical supervisor of the paramedics, Dr Carolyn Nelson Hardy, who was visiting the station for the day (partly to make sure we mediapersons didn't get in the way of anything). Then Chris Harris hit the gas pedal, and we roared out of the station with the sirens going at maximum ee-aw. Someone, somewhere, was in distress, and the paramedics were on their way.

Now, for anybody who has not been driven in an emergency vehicle at top speed through city traffic, breaking all the rules and shooting red lights, let me give you one piece of valuable information: it is the BEST POSSIBLE FUN that you will ever have in a vehicle (legally). Chris did some extremely fancy manoeuvring along First Street, the six-lane main road through Santa Ana. We swerved in and out of traffic queues, nosing our way to the front of each line-up. We peeked out into the intersections when the lights were against us, and Chris turned on the klaxon which added a *whoop-whoop* to the ee-aw, under cover of which we then dashed over against the red. At one point there were road-works, and our side of the carriageway was so congested that Chris McKernan grabbed the microphone of the loudhailer system and asked motorists to back up so that we could move on to the opposite carriage-way, which we then did, using maximum whoop-whoop. It was absolutely wonderful. Both Chris Harris and Chris McKernan were highly professional men, trained in all the intricacies of fire fighting, driving and paramedical aid; but there is no doubt in my mind that despite their professional demeanour they loved the ride every bit as much as I did. They tried to look casual and 'all-in-a-day's-work' about it as we weaved in and out, but I know they were really thrilled to bits to be doing it. However, all good things come to an end, and with Chris McKernan's excellent navigation we arrived at our destination in less than four minutes.

It was a trailer park, a collection of permanently placed mobile homes which are often the only affordable housing for people with low incomes. The firetruck had just beaten us to it and was parked outside in the sunlight, still twinkling, and giving off wavy lines of hot air from its engine, like a steaming racehorse. Noble steed. Chris Harris grabbed the emergency kit and he, Chris McKernan, Carolyn and I sprinted in, followed by our cameraman Mostafa with his gear. The scene inside was very peculiar. The patient – whom I shall call Mr White in the interests of medical confidentiality – was a bilateral amputee; that is to say, both of his legs had been amputated above the knee. The reason was instantly visible. He was a very heavy smoker, and his ashtray contained a disgusting pyramid of butts piled up to about seven inches in height. Losing his legs (due to the effect of cigarettes on his arteries) had not cured him of his addiction, and he was also suffering from severe emphysema. He had called the paramedics because he had been feeling a bit more breathless than usual over the last day and a half. To me, he looked like any typical heavy smoker that one might see in the Chest Department Out-Patients, but here he was surrounded by five men in firemen's outfits with a firetruck and an ambulance outside and a few thousand dollars' worth of monitoring equipment inside. An ECG trace was being taken as we arrived, and Mr White was immediately fitted up with oxygen, while one of the paramedics got the story from him. To me, it seemed bizarre to have a fireman asking all the medical questions about chest pain, colour of the sputum, coughing up blood and so on. It seemed as odd to me as if a doctor suddenly started asking a patient detailed questions about their central heating or plumbing. But I have to say that the paramedics clearly knew their stuff and quickly got a very accurate medical history (including the all-important details of his health insurance).

Mr White was clearly not in any danger of immediate death, but equally clearly he needed a few days in hospital for some antibiotics (and cigarette withdrawal). One of the team started an intravenous drip, while another contacted the nearest local hospital on their portable telephone. I was very impressed with the speed and the co-ordination of the business, and particularly impressed with the rapid and accurate report that Chris McKernan gave over the phone. ('We have a 62-year-old Caucasian bilateral amputee with a smoking history of eighty pack-years. He gives a three-day history of increasing dyspnoea, worse in the last twenty-four hours. He has purulent sputum with no haemoptysis. Right now, on 30 per cent oxygen he has no cyanosis, resps are 18, pulse 88 with a few VPBs, BP 135 on 80. Air entry is poor to all zones, but no added sounds. We've got an intravenous with two-thirds-one-third and he's had aminophylline. We'll bring him in.') My immediate thought was that, if I could teach my medical students to report like that, I'd be proud of myself and them.

Just as Chris McKernan said, we brought him in. Mr White sat in the ambulance, fretting about which of the three nearest hospitals he was going to, because one of them once mislaid his wheelchair. I could see his point, but I thought he might have shown a bit more gratitude for all the wonderful (and expensive) attention he'd received so far. Anyway, we zipped along to the local hospital's emergency department, which was extraordinarily quiet, and transferred Mr White to their tender loving care. The transfer itself was also highly professional, and Chris gave his report again (backed up by the written questionnaire), which was clearly appreciated by the receiving nurse and physician. Having made sure that Mr White and his wheelchair were safely in the hands of the medical team, the paramedics cleaned out their ambulance, restocked the shelves with new intravenous drips and oxygen masks and declared that it was lunchtime.

As it happened, it wasn't lunchtime. Another call came in just as we were leaving. We turned on the ee-aw and the whoop-whoop and sprinted over to a second-storey apartment a few blocks away. Once again, the firetruck was there just before us, and our informal group of four paramedics and associated onlookers convened in the bedroom of 71-year-old Mrs Smith. Mrs Smith was a squirrel. I don't think she had ever thrown anything away in her whole life. Her entire apartment was jammed with millions of things, many of them clearly old and broken. I was struck by the fact that she had two televisions, not just in the same room, but one on top of the other (the bottom one being about twenty years old – which probably meant she thought it was an antique). Mrs Smith was well known to the local hospital, where she was being treated for dizzy spells. She had been seen there as an out-patient. In fact, her last visit there had been the day before. But she had woken up this morning feeling a little bit dizzier and so she had dialled 911 (which is American for 999) and called the paramedics. Once again, Chris and Chris were incredibly patient. They got all the details and phoned through to the controller, who confirmed their impression that there was nothing that needed to be done as an emergency. They helped her sort out her tablets and medications, and we all beat an orderly retreat.

After lunch at the fire station (which was a superb home-cooked chilli con carne with a very hot sauce – but what else would you expect firemen to eat?) the next three or four calls were similar to the first two. None of the patients was really sick, and most of them were already under other doctors or the local hospital. Towards the end of the afternoon, however, we got our first real, undisputed medical emergency: a traffic accident. As we zoomed out of the station, we got the early details on the radio. It was a two-car accident, with one person injured. Some highly skilled ee-awing through the rush-hour traffic brought us to the relevant intersection. A man in a newish Buick had shot a light and hit a very old Chevrolet broadside on. The impact had pushed the Chevrolet half on to the pavement, and the driver, a young woman, was still inside, because everybody involved remembered (correctly) the cardinal rule that no victim should be moved unless they are in immediate danger. A crowd of about sixty passers-by had

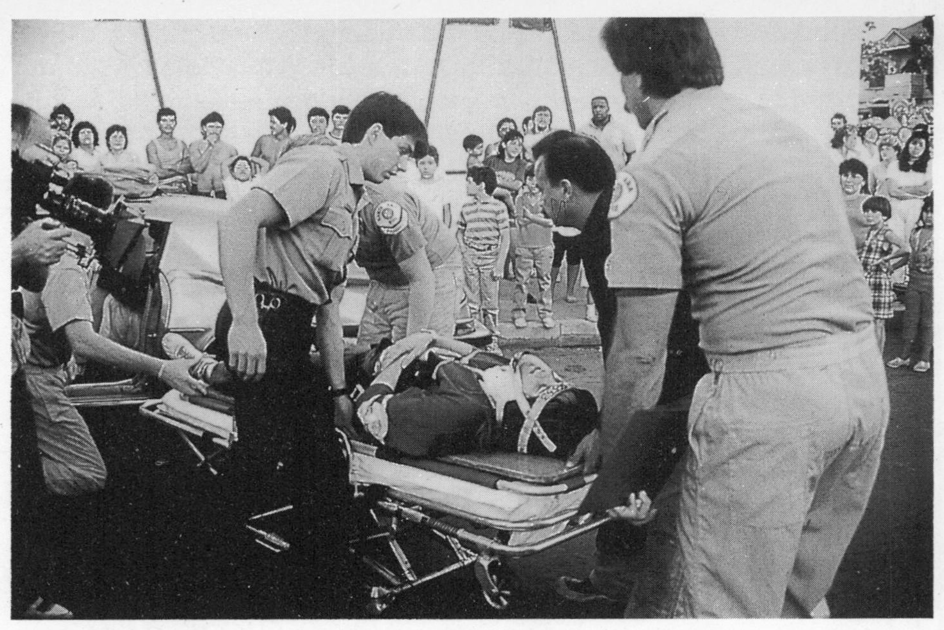

The eagle has landed
A careful and perfectly smooth manoeuvre results in the safe transfer of a young woman with a neck injury from her crashed car on to the stretcher.

gathered just in case anything interesting happened, and the ee-aw men were clearly the main feature.

The paramedics did not disappoint their fans. In their highly professional way they asked the most important questions of the injured woman, Miss Brown (any loss of consciousness, any pain, could she feel her feet and legs, etc.). Having established that there was no major neurological damage, they planned her transfer to the ambulance. A surgical collar was brought from the ambulance and placed carefully round her neck to protect her spinal cord from damage; and, having lined up the stretcher and planned exactly who was going to support exactly which bit of the patient, it was a case of a gentle one-two-three-hup and she was speedily and gently moved on to the stretcher and into the ambulance. An intravenous drip was started (so that drugs could be given quickly if something very serious happened in transit), the ee-aw was turned on again, and we were off. Miss Brown was in moderate discomfort (her left leg had banged against the steering wheel) but in good shape. The incident was bad news for her because she had little money, and her car was essential to get her to work (she was a teacher). But the thing that had upset her most was the attitude of the other driver. He had shot a red light and driven into her – and his first words to her as she lay in her car were 'Have you got insurance?' Not 'Are you hurt?' Somehow, I thought, that man's way of handling the situation was definitely The American Way – or at least *an* American Way. We delivered Miss Brown to another of the local hospitals (which seemed to be quite busy by now) and cleaned and restocked the ambulance.

The last call of the shift was extraordinary. The person who made the call reported a young woman having uncontrollable epileptic fits. When we arrived at the house, the patient was lying on the front-room carpet, shaking, with her sister sitting on the couch and their father prowling around looking like a bear with a sore head. Or rather, looking like a drunken bear with a sore head. We had arrived in the middle of a major family altercation. At first the father wouldn't let the paramedics into the house, but then he allowed them in and withdrew to the kitchen. While we attended to the girl, he appeared from the kitchen brandishing a wooden chair. His command of the English language was not great, but his meaning was quite clear without any words at all. Fortunately, one of the other paramedics was six feet two inches in height and muscled to match. He simply stood calmly (but solidly) in front of the man. Seeing that he was unlikely to win any physical confrontation, the man lifted the chair higher above his head, turned away from us and smashed the chair to pieces against the kitchen stove. He then stumped off to the back room, and we decided that, all things being equal, we would prefer to get the patient to hospital sooner rather than later.

The paramedics had given the girl some intravenous sedatives which at first controlled the epileptic fits and allowed us to transfer her to the ambulance. Once we were on the way, however, the fits started again. Yet there was something unusual about them; she seemed to be conscious and able to talk while the fits were going on in all her limbs (which is not physically possible in true epilepsy). Having hit her with all the high-tech first aid that we had available, we now tried some low-tech reassurance. By talking to her in a calm voice, we got her to tell us what was going on, and as she replied to our questions miraculously the shaking fits stopped, and she calmed down. She had been visiting her parents' home, and a major row had developed. She was an epileptic but had been very well controlled on her anti-convulsant drugs. When her father got drunk and threatened to beat her, she developed 'pseudo-fits' – imitations of her real epileptic fits which were an effective and acceptable way out of an impossible domestic situation. The paramedics had performed a genuine and valuable rescue mission, though not quite the one they had been called in for. Even so, it was a good job well done and it left everyone, the patient included, a bit better off. The ee-aw men cleaned out and restocked the ambulance, and since we were all coming to the end of our respective shifts, we parted company. We had all done well.

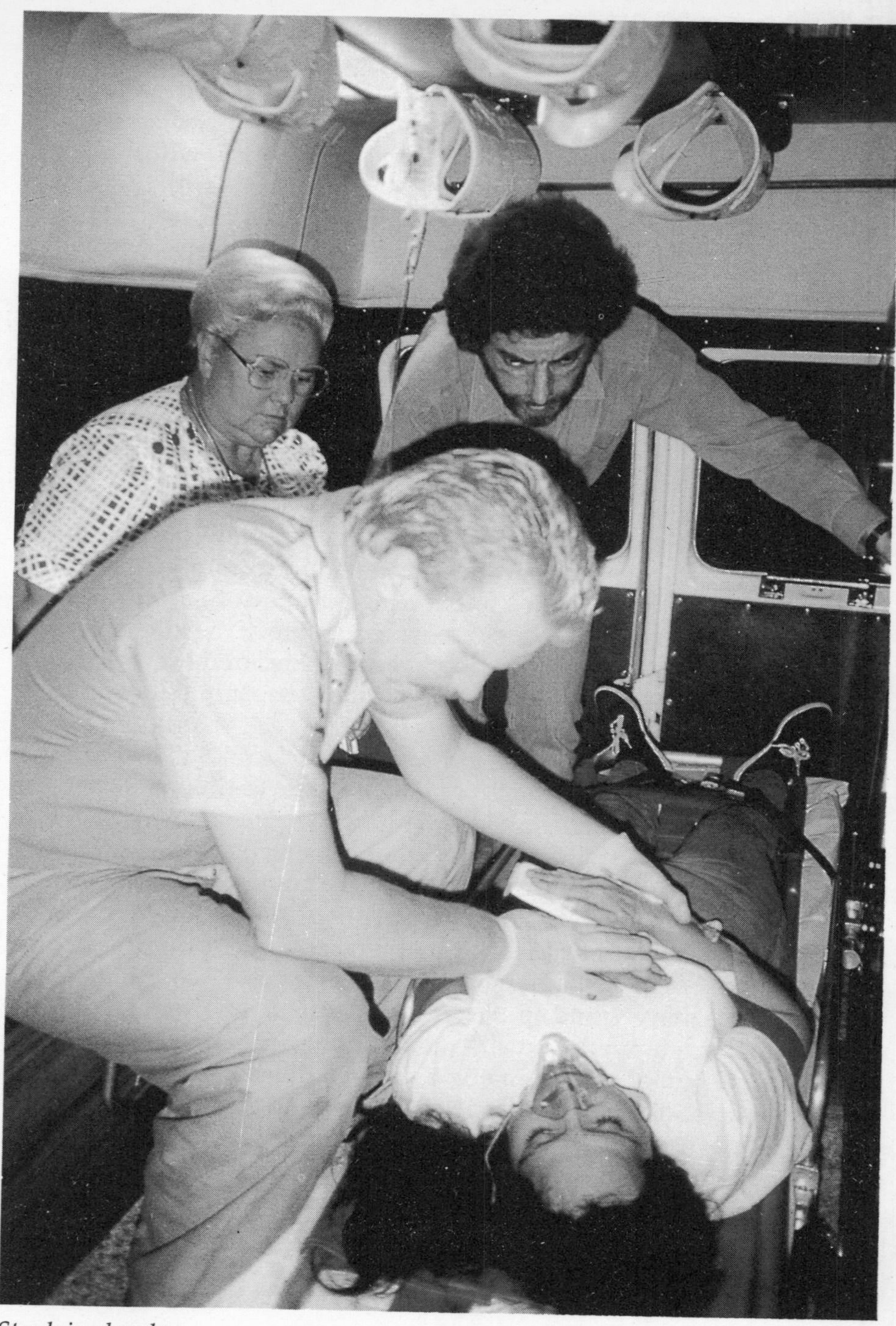

Steadying hands
The ee-aw men, Chris Harris and myself, supervised by Dr Hardy, calm down a mysteriously shaking woman.

Postscript

From what I saw of the paramedic service in Santa Ana, it was clearly a superlative service. The main trouble was that it was too good for the public – or rather, the public wasn't good enough for it. Any service that can be used by the public at large can be *abused* by the public at large. The silliest call that the paramedics ever had was to a middle-aged woman with a tiny cut on her finger. Between them the four paramedics (arriving in the statutory firetruck and ambulance) successfully applied one tiny band-aid. They laugh about it, but nearly half of their calls are unnecessary in the sense that the patient could easily have made other arrangements, or did not require medical attention at all. The problem is that, at one level, the service is totally satisfactory. The paramedics do a great job and are justifiably proud of it. The Fire Department runs the service efficiently and is proud of that. The patients love the attention and the drama (they turn a problem into a drama), and that makes them feel better. The hospitals like having patients who have already been worked up and treated. So everyone is happy except – since the service is very expensive – the taxpayers (who may be more and more tempted to use the service since they know they are paying for it).

As a result of all this superfluous activity the paramedic service is very expensive and may in some districts be discontinued. The problem is under review. The current thinking is that the controllers will probably be trained in 'triage' – a system of deciding the urgency of a call – and could be given the authority to refuse to send a paramedical team if they think the call is trivial. However, that may have medico-legal complications which could lead to cripplingly expensive lawsuits (even if no negligence is proven). It is even possible that the service may be discontinued in some places simply because of the abuses of an uneducated (and perhaps uneducable) minority who can't understand why they should pay heavy fees for doctors when they can get such wonderful free and instant service from those magnificent ee-aw men.

When You Wish upon a Star, Makes no Difference Who You Are: The Make-a-Wish Foundation Takes You to Disneyland

I think that you're forbidden from even talking about the American dream (never mind trying to describe it) unless you've been to Disneyland. It's a bit like talking about the emotional values of the Roman Catholic Church without visiting the Vatican or seeing newsreels of the Pope. And actually, Disneyland is a little bit like America's Vatican. It's an amusement park with an additional touch of Mecca, a hint of Valhalla, a tinge of Paradise, a smidgeon of Nirvana and a flavour of Buckingham Palace. All of which puts it – forgive me for being unpatriotic – a little way ahead of our own Battersea Funfair. We made our Pilgrimage, and here are the details of our Progress.

The signs on the freeway welcome you to 'THE HAPPIEST PLACE ON EARTH'. When you get to the entrance, there's another big sign that lists the population of Disneyland as 263,000,000. It's not a mistake, and it's not their telephone number; they really do mean population. The magical number 263,000,000 is – as I'm sure you realised instantly – the population of the United States (give or take a few folk who were out when the census man called, and a few hundred thousand who are illegal immigrants and *pretended* to be out when the census man called). The management of Disneyland proclaim thus that every citizen of the United States lives in Disneyland. And, despite the fact that nobody lives there at all and the place closes down at night, in many senses the management are more or less correct. They are claiming that part of every American life is lived in Disneyland, even if the person never actually gets there; and the majority of Americans would agree with them. Disneyland is the embodiment of a large slice of the American dream, and some people claim that Walt Disney not only *recognised* the power, the breadth and the scope of the American dream but, in creating its incarnation in Disneyland, partly *invented* that dream.

However, whether we were cynics, critics, sceptics or merely overgrown children, Dunstan and I had a definite mission in visiting Disneyland. It is common knowledge in the States that when children have serious illnesses, and particularly when they have a life-threatening illness, many of them want to be taken to Disneyland. It seems that there is a close relationship in the minds of many American children between Disneyland and heaven, so that the trip to Disneyland for a sick child becomes something of a pilgrimage, or even a rite of passage. Dunstan and I wanted to find out why. We also wanted to meet Mickey Mouse. Plus maybe buy some Minnie Mouse stick-on ears and see Cinderella's palace. And perhaps take the trip in Frontierland. And have a look at the moving replica of Abraham Lincoln. Oh yes, and the human cannonball – that was meant to be pretty good too. And the film crew wanted to go to Fantasyland first, except that two of them wanted to have a go on the Space Mountain before that. As we drove towards Disneyland, just like most American families making the same journey, the kids were having an argument in the back of the car about what to do first.

Actually, we were not there to follow our own agenda. We were there to spend part of the day with Matthew Barbieto and his family. Matthew is seven years old and has acute lymphoblastic leukaemia, the kind that occurs most commonly in young children. In well over half of the children with this disease, it can be cured completely and permanently with chemotherapy; but in some children, unfortunately, the disease relapses. This happened to Matthew over a year after finishing his initial treatment (which itself took over one year to complete). At that point, the situation became very serious. If the disease could be put back into a second remission, there would still be a fair chance of a normal life. But it is terribly hard for anybody, particularly a young child and his family, to face the fact that all that initial treatment did not work, and that now there would have to be more treatment. Fortunately, in Matthew's case the second-line treatment was successful, and his disease went into remission. The very serious nature of Matthew's condition, and the uncertainty of his future, prompted his doctor to put Matthew's name forward to the Make-a-Wish Foundation – the charity set up entirely to turn the wishes of children with serious illnesses into reality. Whether it's a trip to Disneyland, owning a pony or going to Hawaii, as long as it is truly the wish of the child, the Foundation will make it happen. They make absolutely sure that nobody else is making their own wishes known through the child; they won't accept a mother's statement that the child wants a mink coat, or a father's view that the child needs a Cadillac. So, when the local Make-a-Wish representative was given Matthew's name, he interviewed him – alone. Matthew's wish was unequivocal: to go to Disneyland. No question. So the Foundation arranged the trip, and we arranged to meet them all on their last day there.

Being largely unfamiliar with American theme parks, I decided to do some reading before the trip so that I shouldn't appear an utter prune when we got there (not that anybody would have minded, or even noticed, if I had). Disneyland is built on a mere 185 acres in a suburb of Los Angeles called Anaheim. I didn't really have a concept of what 185 acres would be like, but I remembered that if any of my upper-crust friends had a country home with half an acre of garden I was very impressed. This meant that Disneyland would be the equivalent of 370 friends' impressive gardens. This didn't help me much, but I also noticed that Disneyland's younger and bigger brother, Disney World (in Florida), sits on 27,000 acres, an area which sounded to me more like a small Brazilian rain forest (and is actually about the size of metropolitan San Francisco, though much cleaner). Anyway, Disneyland was built in 1955 at a cost of $17 million – which was a lot of money in those days and, to those of us who have to work for our living, still is. Within the first ten years of its existence Disneyland was visited by one-quarter of the US population. The Disney plan was to build a fun park for the whole family, in contrast with the prevailing Coney Island type of funfairs which were apparently full of disreputable and low-class personages that the English would have called low-lifes, toe-rags, spivs or footpads, but which the Americans call sleazebags. Disneyland, then, was designed to be good, clean and fun (a rare combination anywhere in the world, since often those things that satisfy the first two criteria fail on the third).

Our little party assembled and were ushered through one of the turnstiles pronto pronto and into Main Street USA, the central main drag of Disneyland. You would have had to be pretty flint-hearted not to feel a bit festive. The street was lined with replicas of the good old-fashioned shops – the barber shop, the candy store, the nickelodeon – and all that Midwestern stuff. Critics of Disneyland may say that this is highly commercial, but one also has to remember that the original was pretty commercial too. Early-twentieth-century barber shops weren't there to pretty up the street; they were there to sell haircuts and shaves. The shops that weren't commercial stopped being shops. We were walking down a 1980s commercial replica of a 1910 commercial enterprise, but one that had been cleaned up and prettied up, as a result of which it was clean and pretty. And if it seemed commercial, then that made it an even *more* accurate replica of a country that has been commercially motivated since its inception. A replica tram ran the length of the street (the rides were free; the main financial transaction takes place at the entrance, after which almost everything except the food is included). Disneypersons bustled about and wished us a nice day. I could see instantly that, if you had a few children with you, it would be quite difficult *not* to have a nice day, which makes Disneyland one of the few places in the States where have-a-nice-daying someone has a reasonable chance of success.

We didn't have too much time for analysis and deep thought, however, because this was not really our nice day to have. It was Matthew's nice day. The Barbieto gang were already waiting at the Big Thunder Mountain Railroad ride. In the previous two (very nice) days of the trip, we were informed that Matthew had found the Big Thunder

Mountain Railroad the absolute best, the zenith of all rides. Asking him to go on it again for the cameras was liking asking a kid in summer to have an ice cream with sprinkles on. I need to tell you a few things about Matthew, who is that very rare thing among children, an Absolutely Typical Kid. If I were to sub-type his personality I would say that he was undoubtedly of the Instantly Huggable variety. He had a huge smile made more prominent by his shining white teeth and olive skin. His *joie de vivre* and enthusiasm radiated from him in all directions and could probably bleach muslin at fifty yards. He and Disneyland were clearly made for each other. We had a few moments to meet the entire gang – Mum, Dad and brother Donovan – and then we set off for the Big Thunder Mountain Railroad.

Now, it so happens that although I do not have a Thing about Snakes (see Chapters 2 and 10 if you don't believe me) I do happen to have a Thing about Roller-Coasters. In many respects, I am quite a brave and courageous man, particularly in dire emergencies that cause lesser mortals to quail and tremble, e.g. cocktail parties and dinners with bosses; but when it comes to roller-coasters I exhibit the kind of understated quiet courage that other men call 'cowardice'. I loathe and fear them (the roller-coasters, not the other men). I have always said that this is because I drove a motor bike for seventeen years of my life, and on a motor bike the sensation of nose-down-dipping-forward means one thing to the rider: that he is about to sail over the handlebars and become a road safety statistic. However, now that I think about it, my loathing of roller-coasters goes right back to childhood. In fact, there never was a time that I liked them. They have always given me a nasty vacuum-type emptying feeling in a place just below my navel which, like the Bermuda Triangle, doesn't really exist as a place except when things keep on disappearing there. All of which I had explained to Dunstan a fortnight previously when we planned our trip. He had listened to my concerns in a sympathetic and caring manner (having learned a lot from me over the years) and had assured me that all of the Disneyland rides are as gentle and smooth as a Rolls-Royce at 70 m.p.h. on the autobahn in Germany and that not one of the rides would qualify as anything even resembling a roller-coaster. I must say that I had felt greatly relieved by his words but in my haste to be reassured I had sadly overlooked one minor point: Dunstan is an habitual liar.

If the Big Thunder Mountain Railroad was not a roller-coaster, then the Sahara Desert is a swimming pool. My suspicions were aroused slightly when Mr and Mrs Barbieto declined to go on the ride (despite my generous insistence) and said that they had more important things to do such as holding the coats. Dunstan himself very much wanted to come along (he explained) but suddenly found that he had to ring Head Office and find out whether we had exceeded our daily quota of paperclips and rubber bands in January 1984. It was down to me, Mostafa the cameraman, Flynn the director and Chris Clarkson on sound. Eagerly Matthew and his brother Donovan pulled me to the entrance of this gentlest of rides. Years of Pavlovian conditioning have taught me that if you are going towards a fairground ride, and the signs say 'IF YOU HAVE BACK PROBLEMS, DON'T GO ON THIS RIDE' or 'IF YOU ARE PREGNANT, DON'T GO ON THIS RIDE' or something similar, that ride is not going to be as gentle as a Rolls-Royce on the autobahn, despite what anybody has told you. We were ushered into our trucks, battened down with safety rails (another feature that distinguishes a possible roller-coaster ride from a Rolls-Royce), and while we sat waiting to depart, I heard *that* sound: the sound of rushing steel wheels on clattering metal tracks drowned out by the shriller sound of the people on the ride ahead of you SCREAMING AT THE TOPS OF THEIR VOICES. I know that sound very well. It means that they are trying to have lots of fun while being scared out of their minds. It also means that in three minutes' time *you* will be screaming at the top of *your* voice. I turned to Flynn to explain to him that I had a very important meeting with a man at the bottom of a pot-hole in Wales that I had forgotten about, when the car lurched off, and I was stuck.

The beginning is always easy. We went round a couple of corners at

True grit
I demonstrate the True Grit (as in 'teeth') on a bone-shaking foretaste of death disguised as a roller-coaster.

Catfish Man of the Woods demonstrates his medical skills in trying to estimate his patient's weight and water level while she attempts to strangle him.

The lucky holder of the 'Floral Herbs' franchise exhibits the properties of his weight-control herbal remedy. It also cures jockey itch, asthma, worms and sinusitis and can be used as petrol-additive to reduce piston-knock and excessive wear on the big end.

Jolo's assistant preacher and snake-catcher Dewey Chafin gives a couple of rattlers and copperheads his short version of the Sermon on the Mount.

The amazingly fit Carline Berard shows me how to win a wrestling match against a catfish using her famous double-handed neck-hold.

Landscape with figures
The beauty of a bayou grove is marred by a boat bearing a partly clad and beer-crazed gang of desperadoes doing an imitation of a television camera crew on their holidays in Bridlington.

Myrtle and Harold Bigler (plus 'Old Yeller' the wonder-dog) check the fine print on their contract with the man who installed their basement's damp-course.

The author (scarcely visible), Mark Tucker (even less visible) and The Biggest Treehouse in the world (very visible) all pose for the camera.

Fashion note for '89
The author models the Spring collection of Duluth's king-of-chic Bob Pozos. This cheeky little number is the very thing for any fashion conscious man who doesn't know what to wear while drowning in Lake Superior.

In his cups
The author enjoys a little tea-time socialising with Matthew Barbieto and a few of the Bloomsbury Group (Disneyland branch).

'Captain Blood' demonstrates his perfect rippling deltoids, biceps, pectorals and moustache, while the author demonstrates his perfect and rippling vest.

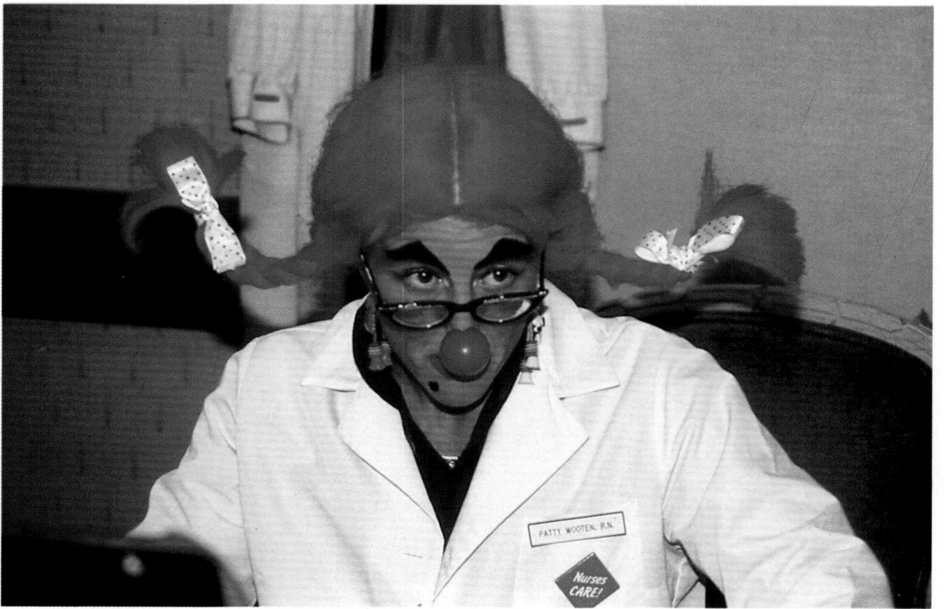

For better or for nurse
Patty Wooten RN demonstrates a new role model for American nurses.

about 10 m.p.h. and then entered a tunnel that looked exactly like a gold mine (or rather exactly what a gold mine looks like in the movies). Then we started climbing up inside the mine inside the mountain at an angle of about 45 degrees. Matthew was loving it and started giggling in anticipation. I am not stupid and I knew what he was anticipating. On a roller-coaster the principle is one of parity – if you go up a very steep slope slowly, it means that you are about to come down another equally steep slope very fast. Which is what happened next. After a dramatic pause at the top of the dark hill we plunged out into fresh air and down what felt like a near-vertical drop. We did some thoroughly unpleasant lurches to the left, some tight S-bends and a mini-corkscrew downwards to the right at about 5 m.p.h. below the speed of light. Funnily enough, although I was scared out of my wits, I can remember exactly what I was thinking at the time. At that moment, what was going through my mind was 'YARRRRGGGGHH!' I was certain that this was going to be the Ride That Ended in Tragedy – the one that Disney had miscalculated. It wasn't, but Disney's engineers (he called them 'imagineers') knew enough about human psychology and about mechanical engineering to make people *fear* that they (the imagineers) didn't know enough about mechanical engineering.

As in any moment of great distress I thought of my children (as any normal parent would). I wished that they could be on the ride instead of me (as any normal parent would). My next wish was that the ride would stop and I could be magicked into a Rolls-Royce on the autobahn, or a pot-hole in Wales, or even a Turkish prison. But I kept all this to myself, since Matthew was having the best time in the entire world. He loved every dip, rattle and dive and shrieked with laughter at every twist and turn. Actually, his enjoyment of the ride was so overpowering I almost forgot my own terror, and I began to get a grip on myself.

There were a few dozen more major twists and sickening lurches plus a few more shocks and surprises, including going through what appeared to be a mountain-style car-wash which threatened to soak us but then didn't. Then, after a relatively gentle curve into the home stretch, we pulled into the station after a ride which had lasted no more than, oh, two or three years. It was over, and Matthew's face was the incarnation of joy unbounded. Mine (I am told) was the incarnation of grey – bounded. And it was at that moment that Flynn, whom I trust only marginally more than Dunstan, pronounced the six words that ensured that I erased his name from my Will for ever: 'We'll have to do it again.'

The second time had the virtue of slight familiarity. My teeth were slightly less gritted. I began to notice some of the neat touches – the rocks that looked as if they were about to tumble on you, the prop coyotes, the snakes and so on. The corkscrew seemed to have marginally less screw. My 'YARRRRGGGGHH' shrank to a 'YARRGGH', and Matthew loved it even more than the previous go.

I can't remember what pretext Flynn gave me for doing the ride for the third time. Something to do with the lenses, I believe. It didn't matter. By then I was punch drunk. And, actually, on the third ride – with Matthew's continued enthusiasm and joy – I almost enjoyed it. In fact, my terror ebbed to such a low level that I was able to enjoy not only Matthew's enjoyment of the ride but the Disney team's genius in creating it. It was (as it said in all the literature) like a living camera shot in which the rider is the lens, seeing only one part of the scene at a time (and hence constantly prey to surprises and shocks). Even for people who have a Thing about Roller-Coasters, this was a magnificent roller-coaster to have a Thing about.

When we finally left the truck, Matthew was as high as a kite. Academics might wonder why a child whose life has been genuinely threatened by a disease would get a thrill out of a pretended threat like a roller-coaster. One look at Matthew's face was enough to answer the question for me; it was the best fun in the world to be hugely scared by something that you *knew* was safe. The earliest ancestor of Disney was the first caveman who threw his child into the air and caught him safely while the mother looked on nervously and the child said the Neanderthal equivalent of, 'Again, Daddy, do it again.' As much as we (as a species) hate genuine terror, we will always be attracted to 'safe terror', which, whatever evolutionary function it may serve, is also wonderful fun – on the third go, anyway.

Matthew's agenda (mercifully) was less frightening from then on. We tried the Mad Teacups (which were infinitely more sedate and, by comparison to the Big Thunder Mountain Railroad, were very similar to a Rolls-Royce on the autobahn – of which I have no experience at all). Then it was time for the human cannonball, who was simply wonderful and drew the OOOHs and AAAHs like reflexes from the audience, including me and Dunstan. Then the Monorail, which was (I remembered reading) the first functioning monorail for public use and therefore a milestone in transport. Actually it was extraordinary by any standards. It was quick, quiet, totally devoid of aerosoled graffiti (very rare in the States) and, like every object in Disneyland, clean (rare in any country). We had time to sit out in one of the cafés and suck a Coke while the world walked by, and then it was time for the Sky Rockets. These are small two-seater aeroplanes fixed on arms attached to a rotating turret. Since the tower is a two-storey effort, the aeroplanes fly out at about seventy feet above the ground, giving you a wonderful view of Disneyland if you are able to open your eyes. I have the honour to report that Matthew and I enjoyed it equally. It brought out all my pseudo-RAF tendencies. ('Roger Willco Foxtrot Alpha, this is Romeo Bravo, three greens on ten zero right. Bit of a bad show over Santa Monica. Charlie November bought it over the freeway. Ginger's hit but he'll pull through. Get Tiger to set us up with a Guinness at the Feathers, eh?') What I actually said was the same thing that Matthew said (and I quote verbatim): 'WHEEEE!'

The planes landed, and we returned to our respective keepers: Matthew to his mother and I to Dunstan (who had been unable to come on the ride owing to the sudden need to make more phone calls to Head Office concerning the excessive use of superfluous phone calls during filming trips). The Barbieto gang had to go back home to Snohomish (yes, really, and it's in Washington State, so there), but there was no doubt that the whole trip had been a smash hit. Matthew's dreams of fun at Disneyland had been turned into real fun. With the stark contrast of what Matthew and his whole family had been through in the last two years, Disneyland had fulfilled its promise of being the Happiest Place on Earth.

Postscript

Even now I am trying to balance the criticisms of Disneyland with the amazing amount of fun that kids (and adults) have there. Perhaps the problem is not with Disneyland itself, but with the whole American attitude to fun. One writer pointed out that, since religion in the United States had lost its fun, they seemed to have taken their fun and tried to put religion into it – hence the pilgrimage aspect of the trip to Disneyland. There is something in that view, though it's not exclusive to the Americans. One English science-fiction writer was so swept away by Disneyland that he wanted the whole world to live like that. Whereupon a clutch of more balanced correspondents pointed out that nobody was actually living like that at all, that all the people in Disneyland were visitors and that there were no unemployed, no infirm and of course no destitute since very few people get in without the price of a ticket.

Disney wanted to create fun that was good and clean, and that could be enjoyed by the whole family. His own experience of Los Angeles had frustrated him, and he set out to create – as the setting for the fun – a model of how people *could* live. The model works, but people seem to have forgotten that it is a model, not a city; and it is a fun park, not a shrine. Inside the park, people participate in everything that happens around them (as it says in the literature, 'there are no spectators, only participants'); they are transported around with efficiency and without crowding; they can sit and eat in park areas; they can walk anywhere safely – they can have a nice day. Outside the walls of Disneyland, Los Angeles offers almost the opposite. Travelling in Los Angeles is a dog's breakfast. Sitting in public areas comfortably and safely is not easy, and in most parts of Los Angeles I found it very difficult to have a nice day.

Undoubtedly, Disneyland is 'unreal', but is a fun park *meant* to be 'real'? Is a rocking horse a Bad Thing because real horses don't have wooden rockers under their feet? Is a performance of *Hamlet* a Bad Thing because Hamlet seemed to die and then came alive again for the curtain call? And how about Santa Claus? It may well be that Main Street USA never existed in reality, which makes Disneyland a repository of dreams (or rather The Dream) rather than a museum of contemporary culture (although they may also be clean and 'unreal'). However, in my view the problem is caused not by the builders who fell short in creating 'reality', but by people who seem to take the whole idea of fun too seriously, ignoring the central motivation (i.e. fun, which involves taking some activities less than seriously) and failing to take the real world seriously enough. Matthew had no problem with Disneyland; it was the best fun in the world and nothing like day-to-day life in Snohomish. I had no problem with it, because I was with Matthew. Matthew had got it right – we had had a nice day.

Pumping and Ironing: The Intimate Personal Lives of Body Builders on Muscle Beach

The Americans have blurred the dividing line between preventive health care and narcissism, as they have between grooming and acting. The current cult of the Hunk, personified in Arnold Schwartzenegger and Sylvester Stallone, has fuelled a rising flurry of activity that occasionally borders on frenzy. If that frenzy has a centre, it is on Venice Beach, California, the current reigning holder of the title 'Muscle Beach, USA'.

To speak frankly, I have never been a Hunk. Other boys in my class diligently sought Hunkhood, sent off for postal courses in muscle building from Charles Atlas and turned parts of themselves more or less (usually less) into rippling this and glistening that. I didn't. I chose instead the lonelier path of the 94-pound weakling on the basis that, while strong men roamed and strutted on the beaches of the world, there would always be a demand for 94-pound weaklings to get sand kicked into their faces. Also, I felt even then that muscle-puffing was a vogue which would eventually pass. I still think the same, but it hasn't.

Los Angeles, on the west coast of the USA, really represents the nearest thing America has to the golden life (despite the claims to the contrary of a tatty little clip joint in the desert known as Las Vegas). LA has almost the correct amount of freely available sea, sunshine, sand and sex (though a little less of each than in its heyday). The people are clean, long-limbed, blond-haired and straight-toothed. More of them have more money than the average American, partly because much of the money they now have once belonged to the average American – the movies being an effective mechanism for the redistribution of wealth. But the result of the combined beneficence of nature and nurture seems to have gone to their heads, and to the average outsider most Californian residents seem to be ever so slightly bonkers.

Many years ago I investigated Californian experiments in relaxation, and witnessed the Californians spending more effort on relaxing than anyone else in the world. The zenith of their efforts was the relaxation tank in which the subject floated in warm darkness, unable to feel or see anything and totally free to get in touch with his or her own feelings and thoughts, including thoughts about why he or she was in there and how much it was costing. Taking to this activity with typical intensity, the Californians almost invented a new sport of *competitive relaxation*, and I was surprised that they didn't make it an Olympic event. Anyway, that was ten years ago, and today most of the relaxation tanks are quietly rusting on the heap of America's outmoded 'me' toys. Whereas the late seventies were the years of being laid back and letting go, the late eighties seem to be the age of gently getting it all under control again. Having let it all hang out, the Californians are now trying to tuck it all back in. As a result there is a major boom in running, aerobics, muscle building and work-outs which are very 'now', while the relaxation tanks are extremely 'then'.

Investigating the latest 'now' took me along a strip of Californian seaside called Venice Beach. I must say I was expecting glitz and glamour. After all, I grew up under the influence of major contemporary American philosophers such as the Beach Boys. I knew that Californian girls were the best in the world (*'I wish they all could be Californian gu-ur-urls doo-dee-doo-doo'*), that they did nothing but surfin' surfin' USA, that they had fun fun fun till their daddies took their T-Birds away (even though I wasn't sure quite what a T-Bird was, and whether you really needed it to have fun) and that most of them were called Barbra Ann. So I was expecting Venice Beach to be something like the cover of a Beach Boys album: long strips of white sand, blue seas with white-capped rollers and gorgeous women called Barbra Ann with long legs that seemed to go up to their necks gazing longingly at bronzed males with surfboards on their shoulders. It occurred to me that I might encounter all kinds of temptations of the fleshpots and the evils of lust, which I therefore prepared myself to resist. As it turned out, resistance was a lot easier than I thought. Far from being a sandy sybaritic paradise, Venice Beach turned out to be a strip of shabby and tatty promenade that would have embarrassed Brighton or Blackpool. And it didn't even have a pier.

For a start, the majestic sweep of the golden sands was none of those things. It wasn't a bad strip, mind you, but it was not exactly the paradise islands of the Bounty bar adverts. It was very scruffy and heavily littered, despite which there were a few Beautiful People strolling about hand in hand, romantically picking their way between the Coke tins and the doggy poo. But for sheer tattiness, the beach was an amateur compared to the promenade itself. It was basically a mile or so of asphalt lined with utterly dreadful fast-food stalls on the side away from the sea, with a motley collection of miscellaneous entertainments on the beach side. The fast-food joints were California's gift to the medical profession, offering a range of health hazards from coronary artery disease to instant diabetes. There were sticky things frozen on a stick, jellied in a plastic cup or in chunks in a plastic bag. There were deep-fat-fried things on buns, plates or sticks and sticky drinkable things in every colour from emetic red to bile green. I tried something

I am serenaded by a romantic bearded loony on rollerskates while he awaits the removal of his head-bandage to see if his brain surgery was successful. (Note: it wasn't.)

indescribable on a stick that looked like deep-fat-fried fat. As I had no idea what it was, I asked the man who sold it to me. He didn't know either; he was minding the store for a friend – or perhaps an enemy.

On the beach side of the strip it was the Land of the Buskers. Within seconds I was ambushed by a very tall bearded loony on roller skates carrying a guitar and wearing a vast white turban. I thought at first that he had recently had brain surgery. After he started singing, I was sure of it ('*I wonder if a man could live on Mars/ I wonder what a man would do on Mars/ I saw an advertisement in the newspaper the other day for some real estate on the planet Mars and/ I wonder what a man would do on Mars*, etc.'). There were odd clumps of faded hippies, clearly left over from the sixties, sitting on the ground trying to remember the words of Bob Dylan numbers ('*Ain't no use to sit and wonder why, babe . . . umm . . . wait a minute . . . ain't no use to sit and wonder why, babe . . . oh . . .*'). There were tarot readers and ladies who painted numbingly awful pictures on dinner plates. There was a brilliant comedian who shocked people by juggling with a whirring chain saw and simultaneously hurling out the most outrageous one-liners – 'There are no black or white races. There's only one race, the human race, right? All the rest are Puerto Ricans.' Amid all this tat, and collections of unconsidered trifles that would have embarrassed an elementary school's half-term show of work, there was Muscle Beach.

Muscle Beach itself was also a let-down. For a start, it wasn't a real beach, and it wasn't even on the beach. It was actually a small bull-pen about the size of a pre-school kids' playground surrounded by a chain-link fence. The fence was required to separate the half-dozen or so body builders inside from their groupies outside. Even though the pen was no more than forty feet long and quite narrow, inside it there was enough machismo and strutting to have kept an army of Italian gigolos going for a century. As we arrived, the current crop of body builders were strutting their stuff to the delight and excitement of about two dozen faithful fans. It was immediately obvious that inside the pen there was quite a lot of Stuff, and an even greater quantity of Strutting. What was fascinating was the variety of styles exhibited by the strutters. It was almost like a semi-nude fancy-dress party in which everybody had turned up in some muscle-bound role. One of them was obviously meant to be Captain Blood, the fearless pirate. Another was pretending to be El Presidente del Macho. One was Mr T., and another was Pancho Villa the Mexican Bandit and so on.

At this moment, Captain Blood was nearest to the fence doing the most important and tricky part of the body builder's daily routine, i.e. getting a few phone numbers from his groupies. He was wearing a flaming bandana* and baggy harem-pants with a thick leather belt, and

*Do bandanas come in any colours other than flaming?

he looked very swashbuckling. In fact, he obviously spent most of his waking hours buckling swashes, and the remainder of his time swashing buckles. He hung his arms nonchalantly (and swashbuckingly) over the fence, chewing gum, and flashed brilliant teeth (his) in a sexy sneer at a knot of girls. He singled out one of them and – I swear this is true – got her phone number in less than ninety seconds flat. Having proven his manhood yet again (he told me later that he had a salad bowl full of phone numbers at home) he strolled out to the weight bench and bench-pressed a couple of hundred pounds on dumb-bells. I didn't know which of his activities was more impressive: the two hundred pounds in five seconds, or the phone number in ninety. Both were admirable in their way.

But both required due care and attention, and could not be entrusted to amateurs. I soon noticed that all the body builders had two distinct kinds of behaviour – one for the public, and one for each other. The public behaviour was the strutting and flexing stuff, full of hey-hup-hoo-hah-hey-ho-hup and so on, whereas the private behaviour among themselves was serious and solicitous. For instance, El Presidente del Macho got ready to do a bench-press. This involved lying down on a bench with his head beneath a pair of huge dumb-bells which rested on a pair of davits or hooks above. In order to perform the lift, it required

El Presidente del Macho rests after some impressive pumping and ironing, unaware of his 94lb weakling audience.

two friends to lift the dumb-bells off their hooks and hold them over him, so that he could then lower them and raise them. When he had had enough, his friends then had to take the dumb-bells from him and put them back on the hooks.

El Presidente went into his warm-up procedure, which involved some very intensive aerobic strutting and smiling, followed by a rigorous two minutes of polishing his sun-glasses, followed up with a further three minutes of oiling his body to ensure that everyone was looking at him and thirty seconds of loosening his leather belt so that he could lie down without perforating his abdomen. Meanwhile all his friends including Captain Blood were wandering about swashbuckling and doing hey-hup stuff. Then when El Presidente was ready, things suddenly got terribly serious. The supporters concentrated on their task of holding the dumb-bells with the care and attention of the vicar's wife offering tea to pensioners. It was almost as if they were saying, 'Here it is, then. Have you got a jolly good firm grip on it all right? That's super. Would you like another 150 pounds on it or is it heavy enough as it is? Do let me know when you've had enough, won't you? Super. Well done.' And when they'd finished helping El Presidente strain his built-up body to its limit, everybody immediately stopped caring and supporting and went back to their own hey-hup routines until they were called on to help someone else. It was really rather touching.

Suddenly there was a stirring in the crowd. About half a dozen of the groupies seemed fascinated with the events in one corner of the pen. On closer inspection it seemed that Pancho Villa, while being in all respects an excellent body builder, had rather economised in the underwear department. As a result, while he was lying on his back in his shorts and T-shirt doing his bench-pressing he was rewarding his fans (unintentionally, I suspect) with a rare insight into the fundamentals of his personality and all stations south. Whether he knew that he was flashing more than his smile, I cannot say. Even if he did, lying on his back with two hundred pounds of metal over his head was not a good time to make any adjustments to the downbelows, so he had to carry on regardless anyway. Which to his credit, he did. Having done his dumb-bells and having strutted more stuff than he had anticipated, he leaped up, made a hurried adjustment to his apparatus and strolled off as nonchalantly as he could. I suspected that he had made a few new friends that afternoon.

By now we had got our official permit for the filming, so we went inside the pen and spoke to some of the lads. Again, the contrast of their real lives with their hey-hup-hoo-hah exhibitionism was striking. Captain Blood turned out to be a particularly gentle soul. In real life he was (surprise, surprise) an actor. Not unemployed (a word that actors shun), merely 'resting between engagements' or 'looking at scripts'. A few dollars to let us take some photos would be most helpful – $25 would be a fortune, especially since he hadn't had a proper meal for two days. This man had biceps bigger than the average watermelon, a smile that could bring birds down out of the trees and a costume that would make Errol Flynn look dowdy, and he was *starving*. What kind of world was this? I thought to myself. This is California, I replied to myself. Anyway, Captain Blood showed me how to do some of the body builder's repertoire of poses, and we did a couple of lateral rhomboids, pectorals and a few 5-pound lateral presses. I don't know what I was doing wrong but I didn't get any telephone numbers thrown at me from the crowd afterwards. That, I suppose, is the cruel reality of showbiz.

I thought we had exhausted our supply of surprises, but there was one more. In the far corner of the pen there was a man doing something quite unpleasant with chains. What he was doing was chaining about 140 pounds in weights round his waist so that they dangled in a most threatening fashion down the front. He then hoisted himself on to a sort of stand with his arms on supports at waist level, and lowered his whole body weight (with the added optional extra ten stone) up and down. This in itself was not a surprising sight for Muscle Beach. What was slightly surprising was that he had an English accent. What was even more surprising was that he was an orthopaedic surgeon from Manchester. I mean, when you think of who you might meet flexing muscles in front of a crowd in Los Angeles, orthopaedic surgeons from Manchester must be pretty low down on the list. Just above Imelda Marcos perhaps. But one learns to expect the unexpected in Los Angeles.

We left the body builders to their pumping and ironing. I was relieved to find them so human and so unpretentious despite their macho displays, and I was very impressed with what they were doing with and to their bodies. I must say, after a few hours of watching them and their audience I did feel a little pang of envy, and a slight hankering after some amateur Hunkhood myself. But perhaps after all the path that I have chosen for myself will bring its own rewards eventually. The Age of the 94-Pound Weakling has not yet dawned, but when it does, then the Hunks shall tremble – if they can find time between work-outs, that is.

Below the belt
My new-found friend, the orthopaedic surgeon from Manchester, demonstrates his latest invention – a new type of rupture-belt that produces ruptures instead of controlling them.

Club Mud, Club Mud, Club Glorious Mud: I Survive a Smear Campaign

All work and no play makes Jack a dull boy. And what goes for Jack goes for me, particularly while abroad. The defence rests its case.

It was not, perhaps, in the mainstream of medical care, in the vanguard of physiological research or in the forefront of technological advances, but it sounded like a lot of fun. The idea was explained to us quite simply, and was accompanied by a colour brochure with a beautiful girl in a purple swimsuit on the front (on the front of the brochure, not the front of the girl). It seemed that there is a health spa, you see, where the leisured Americans spend some of their hard-earned leisure. All clear so far? Well, in the back of this spa there is this pool of warm mud. And what happens is that you go along and then extremely attractive women in swimsuits (like the one in purple on the cover) get into the mud with you and daub you with it. Of course, Dunstan and I, being hard-bitten journalists on a medical fact-finding mission, had a few scientific questions to ask first about the potential therapeutic value of this treatment, e.g. 'How quickly can we get there? What time's the next bus? Can we borrow swimsuits? Can we meet the girl on the cover of the brochure, etc.?' Oh yes, and we also had a few trivial questions, such as 'Does it enhance health? Does it cure any diseases? Does it prolong life? If you meet the girl in the purple swimsuit does any of the above matter or do you simply stop caring, etc.?'

The management were very nice about it all, and amazingly honest. Yes, the mud had been thought to have health-giving properties by the native Indians. However, they (the management) were not making extravagant claims for the benefit of the mud – perhaps it might help one or two skin conditions, and it certainly makes everyone's skin feel softer afterwards. On the other hand, they could fully substantiate any claims for the health-giving properties of meeting the girl in the purple swimsuit. Which, after thinking about our fact-finding mission for one ten-thousandth of a second, Dunstan and I wanted to do.

I should state clearly that I am a happily married man. Dalliance of any description does not interest me in the slightest. However, as a doctor and a scientist, it occurred to me that being daubed with health-giving mud by a woman in a purple swimsuit wasn't *exactly* dalliance. It was more a sort of research, really. Also, the whole thing was going to be filmed so that our research results could be shared by the whole world in the spirit of the advancement of scientific knowledge, nudge nudge.

There is an accurate description for the activity that you see in this photograph: it is 'barely legal'.

Now, you might think that you can imagine how nice it is to be daubed with warm mud by a woman in a purple swimsuit, but you cannot. I think this is because you cannot realise how many sensory nerve endings you've got all over your skin until someone activates them with warm mud. It was simply unbelievably sensuous – not sexy, as a matter of fact, but sensuous beyond one's wildest dreams (and when it comes to sensuousness, one's dreams can be pretty wild). As Barbara scooped up the mud and smeared it on my arms and chest, my brain got messages from areas of my body that it had forgotten about years ago. My elbows registered 'pleasure', my armpits registered 'ecstasy' (when did *that* last happen?), and the hairs on my chest chortled with joy. It was quite quite wonderful, as you can see from the pictures. In fact, it is often said that one picture is worth a thousand words, and since you've just had your thousand words (nearly) on this highly complex and scientific subject, I'm afraid you'll have to stop reading and look for the pictures. Hang on a minute, I'll come with you.

6

DAWSON CITY:

A Bit of a Chance, a Bit of a Gamble

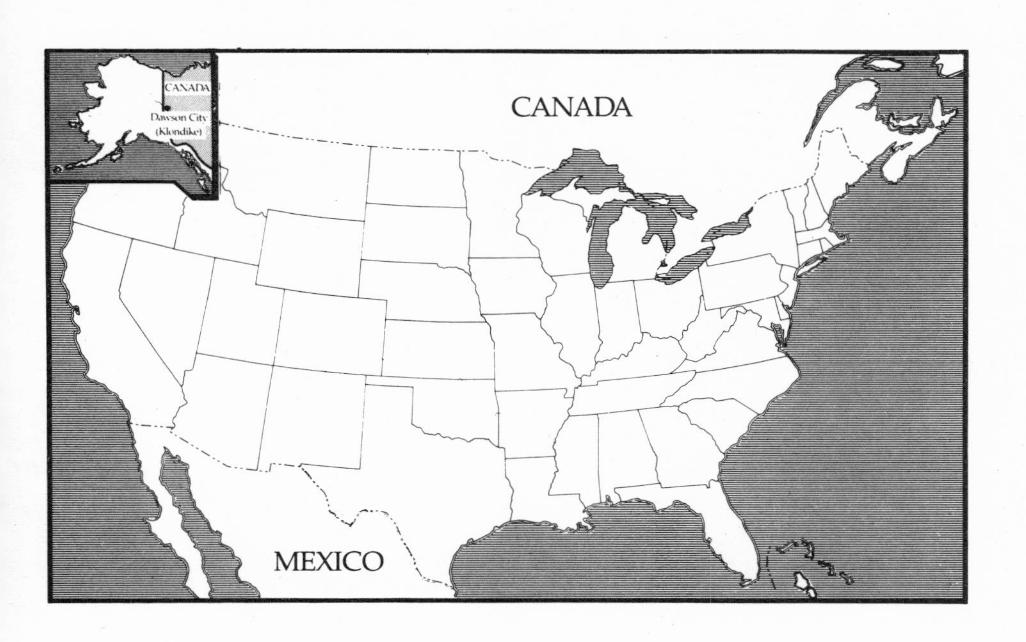

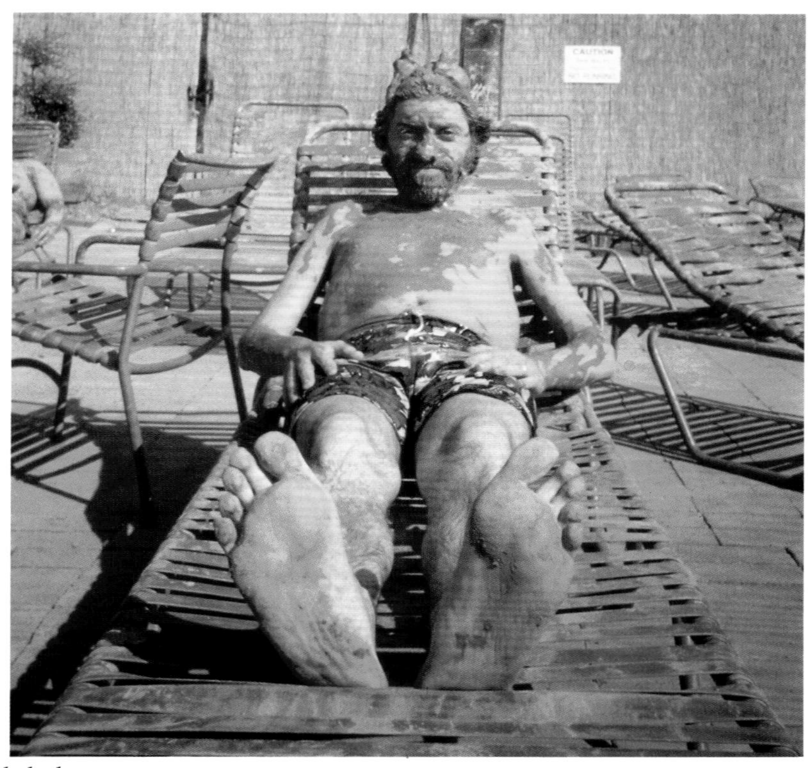

Half-baked
Covered in therapeutic clay, the author endures Lesson One in 'What It Feels Like To Be A London Brick'.

A friendly assistant of The Lady in the Purple Swimsuit demonstrates the direct method of applying mud to the head while the author tries very hard to concentrate on maintaining eye contact.

Now snake it up baby
Young 'Billy' demonstrates the calming effect of being strangled by a handbag on the hoof.

P. Dunstan (*left*) shows off his extensive collection of thick knuckles with which he cajoled the author (*right*) into writing this book. (Note that my saintly halo – a reflection of my charisma and goodness – is bigger and brighter than Dunstan's.)

There's Gold in Tham Thar Fillings: I Strike Lucky in the Klondike

Most people (including me until I was told the facts) think that the great Klondike gold rush of 1896 was an all-American phenomenon. It comes as a surprise to find out that the Klondike was in Canada. And that it still is. And that life there is still a little rough and ready. And that there is still GOLD TOBE MINED THERE. Come on, men, let's go grab some! YEEE-HAAAH! (If you will pardon the vernacular.)

Dawson City is the only town in Canada where gambling is legal. That says something for Canada (which I love) and something for Dawson City (which I came to love). In 1896, some people who may have included George Carmacks, Tagish Charlie and Skookum Jim (but definitely not Catfish Man of the Woods) found gold in the bed of the Bonanza Creek, a small river running near what is now Dawson City but which was then little more than a collection of huts (Dawson Camp Village perhaps). Almost immediately the gold rush started. People literally dropped everything and rushed out to the Klondike to stake a claim. There were documented cases of surgeons downing tools in mid-operation (and getting an assistant to finish off) in order to book a passage to Dawson. At the peak of the rush, Dawson City had a population of nearly 200,000; accurate figures are difficult because everybody was moving around so much and wouldn't stand still to be counted. The place bustled with gambling saloons, bars and brothels.

Most of that has now gone. There are now only one thousand people living in Dawson City, but it looks much as it did in the gold rush days, because the town's council have gone to great lengths to keep it that way. There are no pavements; the streets are paved with earth (how poetic that sounds!) and lined with boardwalks outside the larger buildings. The houses and public buildings are mostly old and made of wood with those verandas and porches that we're used to seeing in the movies. Any new houses are built to blend in. There is no branch of McDonald's, nor of any other fast-food franchise. Although the brothels have gone (Dunstan and I checked pretty thoroughly), there *is* a wonderful old gambling saloon, called Diamond Tooth Gertie's. There is a local doc (who, sadly, is not called Doc Halliday), there is a local dentist who is also the vet because nobody else can do it, and there are some amazingly wonderful frontiersmen who seem to have been left over from the last century. And there is still gold. We investigated all of them.

We started with the local GP, who should have been old, grey-haired,

House calls
Dawson City's answer to 'Doc' Halliday, Gerard Parsons, shares our rented jeep hired from the People Who Would Have To Try A Thousand Times Harder To Make Any Effort At All.

alcoholic and carrying a six-gun. Instead of which Dr Gerard Parsons turned out to be a clean-cut sober youngster in his late twenties and the very best kind of socially conscious local GP. We drove around his patch in my tatty rented jeep (hired from the people who Even If They Try Much Harder Will Still Be Bottom of the Heap). Gerard told me that the commonest problems in Dawson were alcoholism, depression and violence (murder and suicide), all of which are worse in winter. The winter is pretty professional in Dawson. We think we suffer in Britain when it's five degrees below, it's dark as we go to work and British Rail has an epidemic of frozen points. But that's nothing compared to Dawson. In Dawson, when winter comes the sun doesn't rise until March. (Mind you, during the summer it never sets, but that's pretty immoderate behaviour by anyone's standards.) The temperature settles down to a numbing minus forty, and the locals wrap up warm and stay indoors most evenings for about four or five months. Diamond Tooth Gertie's is closed for the winter, so there's not much to do except watch television and drink. And maybe get violent with one another. Gerard referred us to the local dentist, who seemed to have an in-depth understanding of what winter does to the Dawson psyche.

Helmuth Schoener, the dentist, was unlike any other crazy person that I met on the American continent in that he *told* me he was crazy,

Marathon man
Helmuth, the dentist, lounges against one of the current major loves of his life – a Cessna.

whereas all the other loonies wanted me to work it out by myself. Helmuth emigrated from Germany where he had always felt he was a misfit. 'If I hadn't decided to be a dentist, I think I would have been a terrorist,' he said, thus reinforcing the feelings that most sensible people have about dentists anyway. Having decided that he marginally preferred dentistry to urban warfare (rejecting indiscriminate violence for discriminate violence? I wondered), Helmuth set out to discover himself and the world, and fell in love with the wilderness of the Klondike. He saw a lot of it, mostly from his private plane. Of course, having a private plane is not such a rarity in this part of the world, but even so Helmuth's little Cessna was one of the loves of his life. Actually, since we're on the subject, Helmuth's loves make up quite a long list, which is topped by planes and girlfriends. He's been through a large number of both. His current plane was a Cessna 100, and his current girlfriend, Marita, was similar in looks and sleekness.*

Helmuth loved the total freedom that the countryside and the plane

*Actually, I believe that since we visited him, Helmuth has changed both. He now has a Cessna 150 as a temporary measure while he builds himself a special aerobatic fixed-wing plane. His current girlfriend is called Cynthia, but I have no other information about her and I don't know whether she is a temporary measure while he builds himself the ultimate aerobatic wife. I will keep you informed of latest developments.

gave him. He flew us up over the mountains, and we followed the trail of the Dempster Highway which leads six hundred kilometres north above the Arctic Circle. 'It's not the end of the world,' he said, 'but you can see it from here.' On our way back, the sun began to set, and the snow on the mountains turned pink and then blood-red. If I had seen a painting of it, I would have accused the artist of romanticising. The reality was simply breathtaking. This was one of Helmuth's most important 'highs'. The 'lows', on the other hand, sounded bloody awful but they interested Helmuth just as much. He was fascinated with how depressed he got in the winter and had made a sort of case study of himself, observing his own decline into apathy, despondency and endless hours of subsisting as a couch-potato watching old movies. No wonder his girlfriends changed so often.

Some of Helmuth's ideas about freedom were a little off-centre. For instance, Dunstan and I spent an extraordinary evening with him and his friends debating the compulsory wearing of seat belts. Helmuth thought that this was a totally unacceptable imposition on a person's freedom, even if it prevented injury and death. On the other hand, Helmuth believed that if you suffered brain damage from an accident in which you were not wearing a seat belt, the government should have the right to execute you so that you shouldn't be a burden on the taxpayer. I felt that execution was, on the whole, more of an infringement of a person's liberty than compulsory seat belts, but Helmuth would not accept that as an argument. Perhaps it only goes to confirm our deepest fears about picking an argument with a dentist (and I say this bravely since I got my teeth checked last week so I'm OK for another six months, mnyaah).

In action, on the other hand, Helmuth was a teddy bear. We watched him at his surgery/veterinary office, fixing teeth for man and beast. He was wonderfully kind and gentle, and was beloved by his clients of all species.

Not an easy character to make out was our Helmuth but essentially he came over as one of the most undiluted romantics that I've ever met. Like most romantics he was clearly impossible to get along with for a lot of the time, and, equally clearly, Dawson City was one of the very few places on earth that could accommodate a Helmuth other than in a jail or a psychiatric ward. If he ever emigrated from Dawson I would imagine his options would be limited – though Siberia or the Gobi Desert of Mongolia might just about be big enough. We shook hands with him, vowed to meet again (which undoubtedly we will) and moved on in our pursuit of gold.

Art Fry, the oldest living gold prospector and fount of all local wisdom, was, by contrast, about as romantic as a bauxite factory. He looked like one of those grizzled and partly toothless old men who hung about in the saloons in the cowboy movies and who were always called the same name, i.e. 'old timer'. Art Fry was a genuine, darn-tootin', authentic old timer, apparently left over from the last century (almost). At the age of sixteen he had come to the Klondike from Vancouver, where he was a prize-fighter – a prize-fighter, waal, fuh gawsh sakes! Ah'm tellin' yew, eff Ole Art Fry wuz one of tham char'cters in tham thar movie stories, ah reckon tham folks what write the words'd go reet ahead and rewrite Ole Art's life to stop it soundin' like one of tham thar clichés. Ah sure do! *Pttoeey-ping!* [SOUND EFFECT OF OLE ROB BUCKMAN SPITTING HIS CHEWIN' BACCY INTO ONE OF THAM THAR BRASS SPITTOONS.] And that's quite enough of that.

Anyway, Art Fry (who alleges that he is a descendant of the Samuel Fry cocoa empire of the fourteenth century and therefore, like me, a 'God-danged limey') came to the Klondike with the idea of staying for one summer. That was fifty-eight years ago, and 'I guess that Fall hasn't come yet.' His lifestyle brings new shades of meaning to the word 'healthy'. It's not one of the easiest ways to keep going, but it certainly tells you fairly promptly whether you are one of the fittest (as in 'survival of the ditto'). He lives a mile out of Dawson in a hut with no running water, bath or toilet. 'If you haven't got something, you don't miss it,' he says – an interesting opinion, since the entire advertising industry of the States is based on the contrary view. He has three constant companions: his mongrel dog, his pick-up truck and his wife. I have the strong impression that he could survive without any of them, except perhaps the truck. He drives along the dirt roads like a bat out of hell, usually with the dog in the passenger seat. When he has visitors (like us God-danged limeys) the dog has to run behind (and the way Art drives, the dog has the best part of the deal). I forgot to ask him what happens when he goes shopping – I had the impression that the dog would be in the passenger seat and his wife would run behind. Anyway, his transport arrangements, although terrifying, are not crucial.

His lifestyle is simple. He digs gold out of the ground. However, the technology of that lifestyle is no longer simple. Squatting down in the river bed with a thing that looks like a colander is not the way to do it these days. You have to have bulldozers to shift tons of earth, then conveyor belts to carry it through big grinding mills, and then a huge slurry machine which blasts away the earth with jets of water, leaving behind the heavy gold or, more usually, nothing. Art has a group of partners (one of tham thar consorshums, I'll be bound), and his wage bill alone is $20,000 (about £11,000) a month. Which is no small responsibility for a man living out of a one-room shack with no running water and no running anything except a dog.

There was no doubt that it was a healthy life – for those who survived. Art didn't have any idea of what it would be like when he came to

Dawson as a teenager, and 'Lots of others didn't either. If you were ill in the middle of winter then that was bad luck, because no doctor could get out here because there were no aeroplanes. I guess you just laid down and died.' I wondered whether people laid down and died in large numbers; Art thought it wasn't all that common. 'People lived plain, people lived tough, people lived active, unless there was an epidemic, which there hardly ever was. The odd Indian got TB, but that was wiped out. This is a healthy country. No fog, no contamination. You can drink from the creeks, and you don't need to boil the water.' Perhaps the Klondike of the early twentieth century was obeying Buckman's First Law of Life on Earth (you remember: 'Every country gets the health service it deserves'). But, looking around at a landscape pockmarked with heaps of excavated earth like a lawn devastated by gigantic moles, I couldn't help feeling that the countryside hadn't quite got the human beings it deserved.

Actually, Art's gold-mining endeavours had gone well that week. He had just dug up 105 ounces of gold. Since the current value of gold was then $500 (£285) an ounce, I did a rapid mental calculation and realised that Art had made approximately in the region of quite a lot of money. 'Enough to buy the beans and bacon,' was his phrase. So, in celebration of times past, Art decided to show me how he used to pan for gold in the old days before the bulldozers, when he first came out and staked a claim for a capital investment of $350.

He grabbed a flat tin pan from the hut, and we walked down to the edge of the Bonanza Creek. The pan looked a bit like a wok – you know, the things that yuppies use for stir-frying Chinese vegetables. It immediately occurred to me that I could strike lucky and get rich quick. Not by mining gold, but by selling authentic Klondike gold-pan-woks that not only give you a healthy low-fat diet, but double as 'wage-earning utensils for those who want to get material value out of their property holdings'. Perhaps not.

Gold-panning itself is not all that difficult. The catch is knowing where to do it. Art took his Klondike wok and marched towards a particular pile of darkish earth heaped up on the river bank. To me, it looked like any of the zillion molehills that marred the landscape like bad acne. But, according to Art, this pile had come out of a particularly rich area on the other side of the creek a few months before, and the people that had moved it had left it there by mistake and had forgotten to sift through it. Art had a strong feeling that this was good stuff. In the event, he proved himself right.

We scooped up a few pounds of earth and knelt down by the side of the creek (to be a successful prospector you need two things: a pan and good knees). He explained that gold is nineteen times heavier than water and it stays on the bottom of the pan when the earth is washed

The art of being Art
Art Fry demonstrates the agility of his knees and the correct use of the Klondike Wok.

away. Art's wrist action, born of fifty-eight years of practice, was poetry in motion. Mind you, he'd have been a pretty stupid prospector if he hadn't got good at it after fifty-eight years. Even so it was a joy to watch him flicking the pan and sloshing the slurry around, leaving the bits he wanted at the edge. A few minutes of sloshing and flicking and Art began looking pleased with himself. 'We've got some colours,' he said. 'Colours' are what the *real* prospectors call bits of gold. I must say this came as a disappointment to me – I could understand the forty-niners shouting 'Gold! Gold!' but I really wasn't too smitten with the thought of them dashing into the streets yelling 'Colours! Colours! I struck colours! There's colours in tham thar hills, etc.!' However, that was a minor detail. We had undoubtedly struck lucky, and there were about eight (well, seven actually) little chunks of dull yellowish stuff stuck on the edge of the pan like bits of cereal that a child is trying to avoid finishing off, despite the fact that it will make him big and healthy like Daddy.

It was an interesting moment for me. There we were, holding a pan that had cost a total of maybe fifty cents but had brought us chunks of gold worth God knows how much, all for a few minutes' sloshing and flushing. Suddenly I understood the lure of the Klondike. To explain the attraction of this wild part of the world, and the power it exerts on the hearts of men, I need only repeat that one romantic word which has inspired mankind for generations: 'Money!' Now, for the first time, I was experiencing the true call of the wild. I looked at the huge pile of earth and tried to calculate how many pans' worth it represented. I came to the conclusion that it was lots.

Art was pretty happy too, and generously donated the contents of the pan to me and Dunstan. He even told us the address of the gold buyer in town. We thanked him profusely and left.

The gold buyer's was quiet – a little office equipped with very sensitive electronic scales (at $500 an ounce you don't want to mess around with a butcher's scale, do you?). My fears of being mugged for my gold subsided. I went in and spread out my haul in the scale pan. The buyer, Bob Koteff, blew away little flecks of dust on the top of my haul and then ran a magnet over the pan to remove any iron filings. He made a note of the read-out of the electronic balance and went over to his calculator to print out the exact value of my find. My haul, at a *conservative* estimate, was worth a *minimum* of twenty cents, which in English is about twelve pence.

Art's parting words rang in my ears: 'In Dawson City, the best way to wind up with a small fortune is to start with a large one.' Danged right, fuh gawsh sakes!

7
THE NAVAJO NATION:
Cowboys and Indians

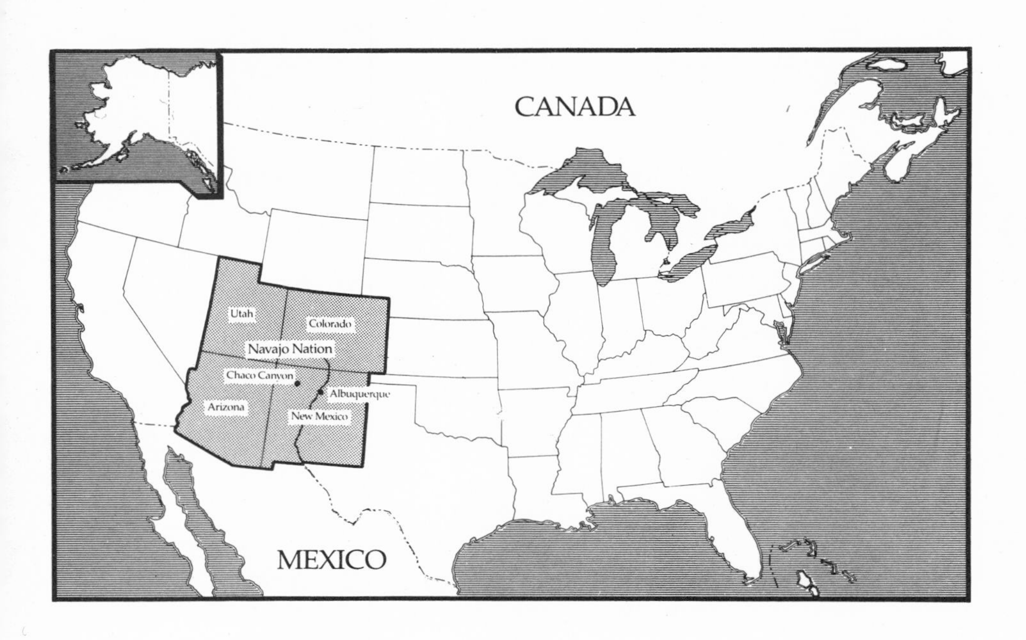

With Their Feet on the Ground: The Navajo Indians and the Land They Love

The Navajo nation is not one of the fifty states of the United Ditto. It is a huge area of about 25,000 square miles, occupying adjacent corners of New Mexico, Arizona, Utah and Colorado, which has been set aside for the Navajo Indians. The Navajo now number 200,000 people (a small city's worth) and are a most remarkable, resourceful and resilient people – qualities which have been absolutely necessary for their survival so far. Their philosophy is deeply rooted in the land they live on, live off and love but do not own, and their respect for nature, harmony and balance marks them out as a very special nation. I enjoyed my time there more than in any other part of the States.

My first sight of the Navajo nation was from four hundred feet up, in a hot-air balloon. In some respects this was a good idea, since it gave me an overview of part of the territory. But in other respects it was a very bad idea, partly because the Navajo people believe that you should never lose contact with Mother Earth, and partly because our pilot, Dr Steve Komadina, crashed the balloon (thus confirming the Navajo belief).

It was a perfect day for hot-air ballooning (so I was told) as we drove out from Albuquerque. Albuquerque is the capital of New Mexico and is pronounced Al-Burr-Cur-Key; the main problem with the name is to know when to stop writing qs and es, and not to produce something like Albuquerquerquerque. However, once we had solved little problems like that, we saddled up and moseyed out at dawn. The sky was ludicrously blue. It had a magical kind of cool stillness and vast clearness which made absolutely everybody say 'Aahh!' and think what a simply perfect day it was. The land rolled out in front of us with valleys and craggy hills that were nature's rehearsal for the Rocky Mountains. Outside the city, it was largely unpopulated (therefore clean) and breathtakingly lovely. Steve Komadina, the local obstetrician, couldn't wait to show me the country from the air, despite the fact that he'd been up all night and had delivered eight babies in the previous twenty-four hours. Steve's balloon had a huge stork on the side of it (to remind the populace of his obstetric connections), but we tastefully avoided all the usual puns about delivering babies by air mail, ahaha, nudge nudge.

We took off with a blast of hot air from the propane burner, which comes as a little bit of a surprise if you're not used to it. We got up to a few hundred feet and drifted, for the most part silently, over the pure countryside as the sky warmed up into a gentler blue, with a few wispy clouds air-brushed in by the Divine Architect to give a more artistic effect. As we floated along, Steve told me about the Navajo people and what he'd learned from their lifestyle. Steve was rather unusual for a young man who had spent his life in American medicine, mainly because he believed that there is more to life than American medicine. That is not a popular belief among the medics of the USA. In fact, doctors in America take their professional life so seriously that it kills them – the average American medic has a life span *fourteen years* less than that of the average male. Steve didn't want to sign up for this particular kind of mass suicide and chose a location where quality of life mattered. Make no mistake, Steve was no slacker; he worked tremendously hard at his job, but he also worked tremendously hard at *not* working when he wasn't at his job. He was also a professional llama-breeder, a bishop in the Mormon Church, the owner of a white-water rafting enterprise, a world-class hot-air balloonist and happily married. (Any one of these, even the last, would be fairly rare in an American medical family; the combination of all five is totally unheard of.)

The Navajo, Steve explained, took things slowly and thoughtfully. They did not see the point of rushing around simply for the sake of rushing around, and they respected the land that they lived on. With that philosophy, it was no surprise that the early Americans tried to exterminate them – that kind of thinking would be highly dangerous for a free-enterprise nation and could seriously have affected property prices if it had caught on. The folk hero Kit Carson was actually the most vicious single instrument of their destruction, and the Navajo were reduced to a pitiable band by the end of the nineteenth century. However, somehow they survived the attempted extermination, kept their culture intact, flourished and multiplied, and then they campaigned for their own territory, which we were now beginning to glimpse from the air.

Not for long. The subject of the conversation was so interesting and engrossing that Steve forgot to turn on the propane burner. For a hot-air balloon, the absence of hot air is something of a set-back (as it is for doctors and broadcasters), and we began to sink towards the earth. I couldn't actually believe that Steve didn't realise what was going on, and assumed that he was in perfect command of the situation. It just shows that you can't trust an American doctor, even a nice one. When we were about sixty feet off the ground and still falling, I broke into Steve's rhapsodic description of Navajo life with a slightly anxious 'Aren't we a bit low, old chap?' I was expecting him to say, in unflappable pilot style, 'Don't panic, old boy. Up we go', instead of which he looked over the side and said, calmly and firmly, 'Oh. Bend your knees.' I had just started saying, 'Does . . .' (which was the beginning of the sentence, 'Does that mean we are about to crash?') when we crashed.

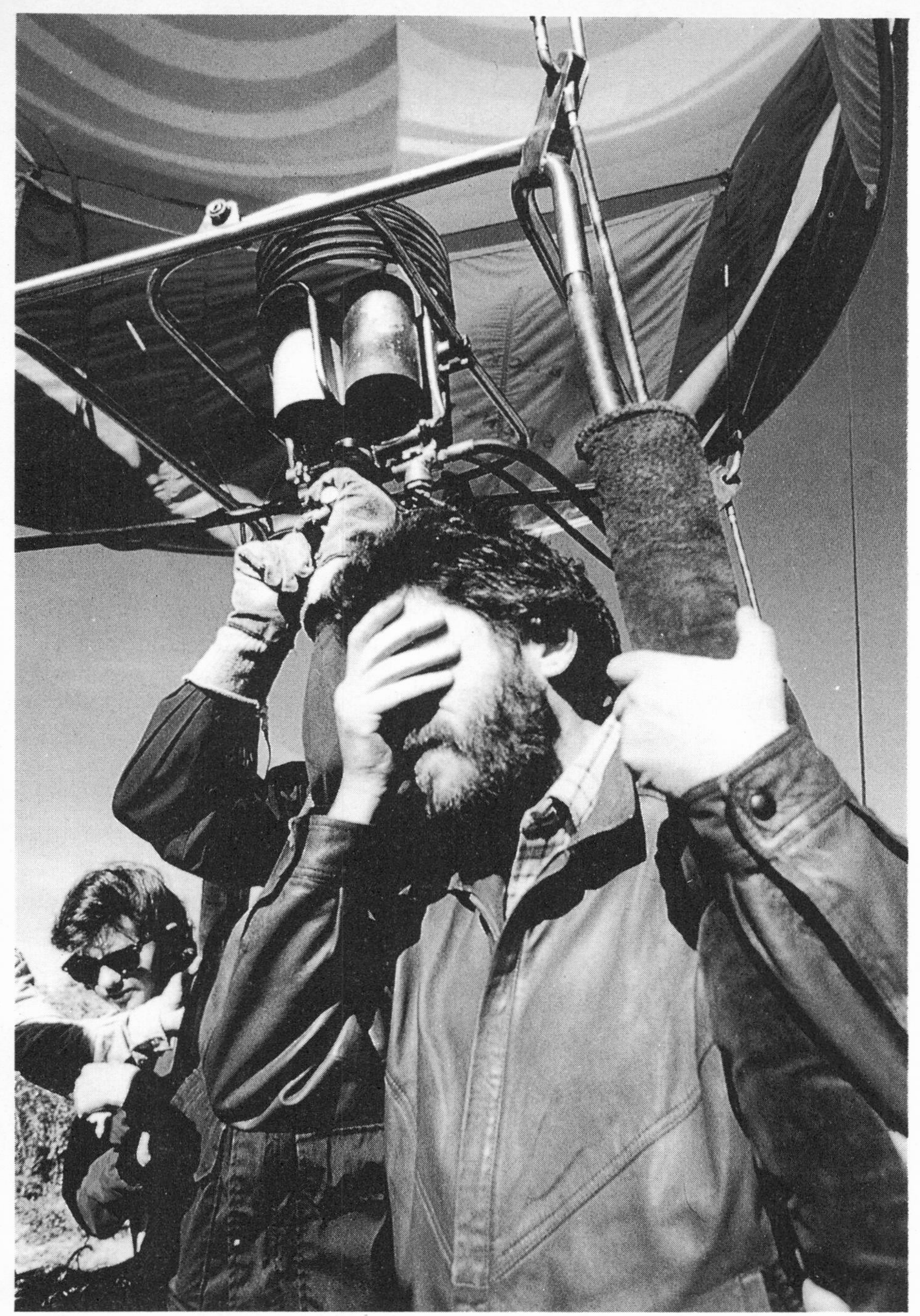

. . . And return you gently to mother earth   The moment at which Steve was almost persuaded to recreate our accidental crash-landing. I do my imitation of Dr C. No-Evil.

We hit the ground with an impact halfway between a flop and a wallop (a flollop perhaps), and immediately the balloon fell over sideways. I fell on top of Mostafa and the camera, and Lindsay, the sound recordist, fell on top of me. It was very funny, and a timely reminder that losing contact with the earth is always a temporary affair. The rest of the production team had been following in a jeep, and when they eventually arrived they immediately suggested that we should crash again so that it could be filmed from the ground (Mostafa had stopped the camera just before we hit). Nobody who had survived the crash agreed with this suggestion. I can't think why. Ironically, the next thing that we had decided to do was to get Steve to read 'The Balloonists' Prayer' (*May the winds take you . . . and return you gently to Mother Earth'*). I suppose there are many different degrees of gentleness. With absolutely no injuries to any of us that we could detect (or claim for) we let Steve go back home to recover from his obstetric adventures and we set off for the Navajo nation.

All this obsessive talk of loving the land, living in harmony with the land and so on didn't really begin to make sense to me until I saw the land in question. Then I suddenly realised what all the fuss was about. The Navajo land is exceptionally beautiful; it is also pink. This surprised me since, being English, I expect land to be green or yellow, and occasionally white (in winter) but mostly brownish. However, in this corner of New Mexico, the hills and ravines were definitely a deep warm pink. Most of the landscape seemed to be rock. Often it was crinkled and furrowed where rivers and streams ran or used to run; sometimes it was thrown into folds or eroded into pillars and in some places it was quite flat, although dusted with a fine coating of powdered rock trying to become soil. Perhaps the most striking thing about this countryside, other than the designer colour, is that there is so much of it. In England there are very few places where you can see no human habitation, drive to the horizon and *still* not even see a house or village. In Scotland there is more of a chance, but even so there aren't many places where you can see the countryside rolling ahead for mile after mile after mile without any sign of human beings. But that's what vast tracts of the Navajo nation are like. At one stage we drove for just under forty minutes along the road without seeing a single house, car or person. When we eventually overtook a small pick-up truck, it suddenly felt like rush hour. Countryside like that doesn't just ask for respect from mere humans, it commands it.

The drive was long, but eventually we arrived at the local general hospital. By any standards, it was a very neat modern hospital, a cluster of tidy buildings that would have been the pride and joy of any Area Health Authority in Britain. The only curious thing was that instead of being halfway down Reigate High Street or Beech Grove, Tooting, or wherever, it was totally alone, sitting in complete isolation at the top of a small pink hill in the middle of miles and miles of the pink rock.

Inside, at first glance the hospital looked like any other modern hospital until one started looking at the fine details. In the obstetrics department, the delivery rooms were the very model of modern cleanliness and sterile hygiene but had a huge arrow painted on the ceiling with the letter 'E' at the point. Why? Because it is an inviolable Navajo tradition that all babies must be born facing the east (where the sun rises, in case you'd forgotten), and how could anyone tell, in the middle of a hospital, which country one is in, let alone which direction is east? Near the arrow in each delivery room, there was a hook embedded in the ceiling from which hung a long red embroidered sash finishing in a fancy knot just above the delivery couch. Apparently the traditional sash is another important part of the birthing ritual for Navajo women – in fact, without birthing rooms with these features, the hospital would not have had any Navajo customers.

The most curious part of the hospital was at the end of Ward Nine. A little sign read 'Native Healing', and there was an indoor version of the traditional eight-sided *hogun* (native hut) built right into the middle of the hospital. It was a very pleasant wood-walled room with a central fireplace and chimney (another important part of the traditional design) and a wooden floor, looking a bit like an octagonal sauna. The Navajo had asked for an earth floor (contact with Mother Earth being so important), but this was the one point on which modern American hygiene regulations won out over the need to comply with native traditions.

My medicine man was waiting for me. Since he was the first Indian medicine man I had ever met, I assumed he would look like someone out of the cowboy movies – and he did. A wonderful calm, pleasant and crinkly face matched his gentle soft speech and slow, deliberate manner. The only disappointment was his name. I was hoping for something like Great Gentle Bear, Big Running Water or something equally evocative, but he was introduced to me as Mike Mitchell. Now, I hope I don't offend all those of you who are called Mike Mitchell when I say that, as a name, Mike Mitchell is a little prosaic. It's not a *bad* name, mark you, it's just a little bit humdrum for a Navajo medicine man, that's all. I could think of names that might be *more* humdrum, such as Derek Watkins (more apologies to all readers called Derek Watkins), and some names that would be more *surprising* for an Indian medicine man, such as Isaac Kowalski or Ranulph Twisleton-Wyckham-Fiennes, but 'Mike Mitchell' was a bit of a let-down. I later found out that most Navajo keep their native names secret among themselves and don't like to be called by their true names by outsiders – not a bad precaution, given their history.

Anyway, his name was the only let-down. In every other respect he was every inch the charismatic, wise and mysterious medicine man. He lit a pipe full of special Navajo mountain tobacco which had been gathered at a certain time with certain prayers, and which was therefore very powerful in healing. He smoked some himself and blew the smoke over my body, accompanied by prayers and crooning in a soft voice. Then he gave me some to smoke. Now I am not – and have never been – a hippie, nor am I a smoker, but even to the outsider this Navajo mountain tobacco was what I would have called Very Good Stuff. I'm sure it didn't contain Certain Illicit Substances, but it was certainly *very* nice and undoubtedly full of all kinds of magic and healing powers. Like far out, man, as we used to say in the sixties. Hmm.

After the smoking, Mike ground up the ash from the pipe into a mushy poultice and daubed it over me to help the healing. He then instructed me (through his translator, Ursula) not to wash for four days (a prescription immediately countermanded by the production crew, who had to share the van with me and who have closed minds on such matters). He also instructed me to walk on the ground with bare feet at dawn (he obviously didn't realise I was on holiday). But to appreciate fully the traditions and the history of the Navajo, Mike said, I would have to visit some of the places they used to inhabit long ago.

One of the most ancient and venerated Navajo dwellings is at the top of the Canyon de Chelley. Getting there, as the saying goes, is half the fun. It's about an hour's drive (which is no big deal) but it's an hour's drive up a river. My native guide was a kind but taciturn young Navajo man called Jerome, and I resisted the desire to shout 'Jeronimo!' as we drove off the road into a wide, fast river. The point is that the river, which is about sixty yards wide most of the time, is quite shallow – in places. The catch is to spot those places, and that's why everyone needs a Jerome. There's a sort of invisible track under the water where the river is only six inches or so deep, and the track winds from side to side, making sharp invisible turns and dips in a way that only a Jerome knows. In addition to your Jerome you should also get a four-wheel-drive low-gear-ratio high-body jeep. And if you haven't got all of those, get a helicopter.

Jerome allowed me to do the driving, while he sat there scanning the river ahead with narrowed mysterious eyes, giving me sudden instructions ('Go towards that branch on the opposite bank. When we are halfway, turn left . . . Now go straight for that big rock . . . Turn a little to the left when we pass it'). Jerome told me that the underwater track is well known to the natives, but that off the track the river mud is dozens of feet deep. In the last few years, over eighty vehicles have disappeared without trace into it (though there is always time for the owners to get out and wave tearful goodbyes to their cars). We swished and sloshed

The white house (vacant)
'Palatial residence in sheltered scenic location. Splendid view. Running water (river). Needs renovation. Ideal for family of 400 archaeologists. Could sub-let.'

our way up river and at the top of the canyon arrived suddenly at the base of a huge pink cliff towering above the river bed. Into the base of the cliff had been cut a small village of cliff-houses, centuries old but amazingly well preserved. The natural beauty, tranquillity and mystery of the place made us all a little reverential and quiet (both of which are exceptionally rare for a film crew). And as we stood there, we gradually became aware of beautiful music played on a flute, floating towards us across the river. I am not a very spiritual person, but the atmosphere of the place was almost religious and so special that I half-expected to find some manifestation of the Spirit of the Navajo playing the flute in the ruins of the old dwellings. The fact of the matter was a little less fanciful. The music was coming from an American man of about forty with a beard and glasses, who was learning the flute and loved to play it in this particular place because it sounded so lovely and spiritual. We apologised for interrupting him, and continued up the path towards the village at the base of the cliff.

Ursula (Mike Mitchell's friend and translator) was waiting for us. Ursula turned out to be an extraordinary woman. Now in her mid-forties, she had been raised in the traditional Navajo ways but had later gone on to train in the American medical system as a nurse. As a result, Ursula understood the strengths and deficiencies of both cultures and could translate and explain one to the other. She took me up to the largest building of the cliff village. It was about the size of a large family house, and for centuries it had been known among the Navajo as the White House. It was America's first White House and had caused a lot less trouble than its successor. Standing outside the Original White House in this deserted and mysterious place, we talked for a couple of hours.

As Ursula talked about the various medical and healing rituals, the similarities between Western medicine and Navajo medicine began to impress me more than the differences. The Navajo believe that there must be a harmony between the mind and the body, and that injuries to the body require an adapting process in the mind, so that they are one again. Thus if a man loses an arm in an accident, he goes to a medicine man so that his spirit can be made to match his body – in other words, in a way, his spirit must lose an arm as well. The medicine man will carry out rituals to appease the god that he thinks has caused the accident and may use prayers, sand paintings or any of several different rituals. In Western medicine, although we use different words, we do the same thing. After a mastectomy (an operation in which the breast is removed), for instance, we may offer 'post-mastectomy counselling' from a trained psychotherapist. We know that this is an adjustment process for the patient, and we don't use phrases like 'matching the spirit to the body', but that's exactly what we try to achieve. We don't say prayers to the Lightning God, or make a sand painting, or rub ash on the patient, but the underlying objective is the same. Similarly, we support people who are disabled or who are depressed with psychotherapeutic techniques which we call 'adaptive'; again we don't talk about the 'spirit' or invoke the gods (not in psychiatric medicine, anyway), but the transaction is the same. The language is totally different. They invoke the gods of rain or wind, and we invoke the forces of 'white blood cells' or 'blood sugar' or 'serum cholesterol' (of which we can prove the existence), but the desire of one group of people to try to make another group of people well again is universal.

Finally, Ursula talked about the Navajo and their land. The big difference between them and white people is that the Navajo don't believe that anyone ever actually *owns* land. They believe that everything to do with life comes from the land (which ultimately, of course, it does) and that therefore it is like their mother. They cannot understand why anybody would claim to own their mother. And there is a fair point there. By Western laws we are allowed to own land; this means that we can pass it on to our children (and stop other people's children getting it) and can plough it up, or build on it, or speculate with it, or drill it for oil. All this is feasible and very visible over the short term. But in the long term we die, and the land doesn't. So who actually and really *owns* land, except in the short term? The cliff village we stood by had been deserted for centuries – what difference would it have made if a Pueblo village council of the sixteenth century had said, 'We own this land'? Ownership is a temporary arrangement. It is extremely important to us, and totally unimportant to the Navajo (although, because of the past, the Navajo now have to accept the importance of ownership as an alternative to extinction). It was a peculiar thought for me. I've spent most of my working life as a mortgage payer, which, I have to admit, does become a rather important part of one's view of the world (although its importance is inversely related to one's difficulty in making the payments). I couldn't imagine going to the building society and trying to convince them that they didn't really *own* our house, and that in a few centuries they (and I) would be forgotten. They would probably reply that I could stuff the future centuries where the sun doesn't shine, what really matters is the cheque on the first day of next month.

Unable to solve the fundamental contradictions of Western society (a very upsetting confession for a medic), I rejoined Jerome, and we began the slosh home. By now I was beginning to feel pretty confident about my abilities behind the wheel (a feeling my wife never shares when she's a passenger) and I also began to suspect that Jerome was exaggerating the dangers of missing the invisible track under the river. I was wrong on all counts. We'd been driving for about half an hour, when Jerome told me to make a sharp left in the middle of what looked like a

Not waving but calling for the AA
I go off the beaten track. And get beaten.

rippling puddle. I made the left turn, but about fifty feet too late. Within seconds we had sunk up to the axles in river mud. I tried to put the jeep into reverse, but the wheels spun uselessly, and then, above the noise of the rushing river and the racing engine, I heard the most sinister and dreaded sound of all. It was the sound of the film crew, who had been following in a larger truck, setting up the camera to film my embarrassment. Stuck in deep mud, a fully paid-up member of AA Relay and miles from the nearest phone box, my predicament was dire. White man, I thought, talks with forked tongue, eats with forked fork, films with forked film crew and, if left to his own devices, quickly gets himself well and truly forked.

Postscript

Ursula told me that the Navajo regarded white people as quick in thought and action, arrogant, inclined to think of their next goal before they've really appreciated the achievement of the last (all of which certainly applies to me) but very creative. I had only touched the most superficial surface of the Navajo nation, but the little I saw impressed me and highlighted disturbingly the contrast with The American Way.

Navajo philosophy has its origins in a time when there were far fewer people around, although even then inter-tribal fighting was a major feature of life – it was no idyllic and tranquil picnic. I suspect that we could never go backwards in time (even if we wanted to); but, as the great archaeologist Sir Mortimer Wheeler once said when filmed among the ruins of Greek civilisation in Athens, perhaps it would be a good idea for everyone who thinks they rule the world to come out to these ruins and think for a moment or two of precisely why great civilisations that consider themselves immortal eventually die out. It's worth a thought.

With Their Heads in the Clouds: The Wannabes Wannabe Better

It was minus five degrees centigrade, the cold wind was gusting at twenty miles an hour, and sleety snow was falling on Chaco Canyon. As I stripped down to my underpants I had difficulty remembering why this had once seemed like a good idea.

Dick Prosapio claimed that the name of his tribe, the Wannabe, was not invented by himself. This was a wise claim. He also claimed that the Wannabes are so called because they 'wannabe' better, not because they 'wannabe' Indians. The wisdom of this claim may be more questionable. To begin with, the Wannabes are not really a tribe, they are more like a group of psychotherapy out-patients on a camping holiday. In daily life they are ordinary middle American white folk – painters, musicians, writers, lawyers and such – who share a certain discontent with that daily life and with the American way of living it. Reflecting on some of the basic philosophies of native Indians, they have tried to 'get in touch with their roots'. And if those roots are not *actually* their own roots, well, at least they're roots of some kind or another, which has got to be better than nothing.

Led by Dick ('Coyote') Prosapio, a trained counsellor and therapist, every month or so the Wannabes load up their dormobiles and Volkswagen vans and head out into the New Mexico wilderness to find some roots to get in touch with. We decided to get in touch with them while they did it. Perhaps there was a certain divine irony about the fact that, the one weekend we chose to meet the Wannabes, there was an unprecedented cold snap, with sleet and snow falling in driven sheets from a miserable grey sky. Somebody Up There was obviously trying to help us English visitors get in touch with *our* roots. Ah me.

The Wannabes had made their base on a high, flat plateau in order to give the gods' gifts (i.e. the sleet and snow) the best possible sporting chance of getting to them. As we drew nearer we could see that they had parked in a sort of ring, perhaps a late version of the pioneers' covered wagons: 'Git thum Volkswagens in a circle, Luke, wimminfolk and children in the middle.' Except that the Wannabes *were* mostly wimmin, and the wimmin and the menfolk were all very polite and nice to each other and to the visitors. Actually, they were so intent on being kind and caring and sensitive to each other's needs (while getting in touch with their roots) that they reminded me of the sixties and the milder varieties of hippies. We seemed to be in the middle of a minuscule twenty-person version of Woodstock. In the snow. Without the rock music.

The first event was the banner ceremony. This is based on an Indian tribal custom, and the idea is that all the participants have to make a banner which they display and which symbolises their life. This is a lot more tricky than it sounds, and I should have started work on it weeks before the event (as the Wannabes all did) instead of leaving it to the day before (which is what I did). As a result, I was in a bit of a hurry when it came to making my banner. I rushed into a local supermarket near closing time the day before and bought a whole lot of different coloured fabrics and hessian and ribbons and glue and stuff. I took it back to my hotel bedroom, spread it out on my bed and then got stuck. I mean, seriously, how do you try to symbolise your whole life? I mean, what does your life actually stand for? When you really get down to it, what is the *real* meaning of your life? And even if you think you know, how do you symbolise it on a banner? Is this the right time to be totally honest? Should you include certain abstract qualities that have run through your life (but which you have every intention of weeding out next year) like all that naked ambition, greed, lust, gluttony (particularly the gluttony), the uncontrollable desire to buy electronic gadgets, the inability to stop picking your nose, the coveting of your neighbour's ox, the driving in the bus lane, the failing to show proper care and consideration for other road users as exemplified by a vigorous V-sign and a shout of 'You couldn't steer the *Queen Mary* up Barking Creek, you cross-eyed hamster-brained fat git!' at an elderly driver in Dalston, and all the other natural shocks that flesh (particularly yours) is heir to? And even if you want to include all that on your banner, how do you do it? The V-sign would be okay, but would the Wannabes understand that it symbolises your unwanted anger? And in Dalston? And how do you symbolise ambition? Or lust (not as easy as you think when you've only got six different kinds of hessian and two kinds of ribbon, and you are not a dab hand at lifelike collage)? I struggled and struggled. By one a.m. my hotel bed was covered with scraps of cut-up material, shapes of hessian that were becoming unravelled at the edges, silhouettes of things that didn't look like anything at all and (everywhere) little blobs and puddles of white glue. Then suddenly, groggy from lack of sleep and full of panic that I was making an ass of myself, I had a therapeutic revelation. Perhaps what I was now looking at *was* the real symbol of my life. Perhaps this was what my life was really all about: a chaotic, unravelling, blobby, sticky, shapeless, colourful, disorganised, cut-up and disjointed mess. I decided to go to bed and finish the banner early in the morning. Either that or completely reform my life instantly so that it would fit on to a banner more easily.

The banner ceremony was held in a sort of Indian ruined temple. It had no roof, which to the Wannabes symbolised the welcoming rain of heaven falling on you, but which to me symbolised a head cold and probable chilblains. The ceremony started with Dick doing some symbolic banging on an Indian drum and everyone doing some symbolic chanting, all the while accompanying themselves on tambourines and drums, which at least kept them warm. I, on the other hand, didn't have a tambourine or a drum so I kept warm by stamping my feet and swearing at the weather (which can generate a lot of heat if you really put some effort into it). I must have looked a little frozen and bedraggled, because one of the nice wimminfolk came up to me with a look of sweet tenderness in her eyes and wrapped a woolly scarf round me. 'I want you to have this,' she breathed. By that time I was so cold that I wanted to have this scarf even more than she wanted me to have it, believe me. And then the ceremony started. In turn, each participant explained her or his banner to the assemblage, who all listened intently and sympathetically and then suddenly shouted 'HO!' in unison at the end. This apparently is an ancient Indian salutation of understanding (and not one-third of the traditional salutation of the ancient Indian Father Christmas, as was previously thought).

One woman had a light blue banner with feathers and skins and black lines: 'This symbolises my totality: my masculinity and my femininity, my light side and my dark side, my cunning and my innocence.' HO! I was thinking that I hadn't got any nice phrases like that ('My greed and my gluttony? My Gilbert and my Sullivan? My Marks and my Spencer?'). The second woman had some special stones that symbolised something (a visit to the seaside perhaps) and some mystical scribbles that were apparently Nordic runes and which symbolised something else (her desire to become a doctor and write illegible prescriptions perhaps). Another woman had a banner that was totally black, symbolising 'the way I feel right now'. My immediate thought was that this person was symbolising her major need for expert help –

less of the ancient Indian traditional banner ceremonies, and more of the non-ancient non-Indian tricyclic antidepressant tablet ceremonies. HO! Dick's banner was a work of art. It was made of some silky material in lovely pastel shades with a few bits of fur from a coyote ('As a therapist, sometimes I need the tricks of a coyote'), and he told a couple of mystical anecdotes to the group. While he was searching for his roots he had gone into a forest (often a good place for roots) and sat down under a tree. In that tree he had found the skull of a coyote, which he took to be a message. Personally, I would have taken it as a message that this was not a particularly good forest to hang about in if you were a coyote, but perhaps I missed something. HO!

Then it was my turn. Eventually, I had decided on a yellow background which symbolised the fact that the supermarket the day before didn't have many colours of hessian left. The banner was hung from a broomstick which symbolised something (my mother-in-law's usual mode of transport perhaps; no, sorry, no music-hall joke ceremonies, please). In the middle of my banner I'd put a winding stethoscope to symbolise my profession as an ancient non-Indian white man's medicine man. On top of that I had put three hearts to symbolise the great difficulty that I had had in cutting out difficult fabric shapes (hearts are about the only shape you can cut in hessian that doesn't unravel before you get the glue on it), and in the middle of those I had represented my word processor. It was of course the totality of my word processor – its femininity and its masculinity, its input and its output, its ability to delete things accidentally and its inability to print the letter I want it to and so on. And then at the other end I put a television to appease the Gods of Television (e.g. the great god Running Mini-Series, father of the goddess of unfunny comedy shows Little Mini-Ha-Ha, etc.). And in the middle I put the mystical letters Ph.D. which are an ancient symbol carried by those tribe members who have done a Ph.D. and whose mothers are very proud of them. HO!

Then it was time for the nudity.

There are many good reasons why the Wannabes get naked and sit in a dark tent together. Of course, when it comes to getting naked and turning the lights out, most Americans don't need many good reasons, and a few don't need any reasons at all, but in this case it was all in the cause of meditation. (As my father might say, 'So that's what they're calling it nowadays, eh,' nudge nudge.) Anyway it seems that native Indians (I think it was the Apache but it might have been the Blackfoot Indians) used to build a thing called a 'sweat lodge'. This was basically a tent totally covered with thick skins and hides so that it was totally dark and airtight inside. They would then light a big fire outside and heat up a whole load of big rocks and stones. (Perhaps I should be issuing a warning such as 'Don't try this at home! You need a nation as big as New

Mexico to do this safely! A flat in Basingstoke is not the right place for an Apache sweat lodge!') Then, when the rocks and stones are red hot, they take them into the tent, clamber in, close the flap and sit round the hot stones thinking about the mysteries of life (e.g. 'Why am I doing this? How can I get out of here?' etc.). Entering the hot tent symbolises their desire to leave the muddled outside world. The sweat lodge symbolises the womb (which may have been similarly cramped but wasn't as hot and sweaty), and the process of sweating symbolises the process of losing your sins (plus a bit of weight, and a lot of salt). Basically the Indians invented the perfect combination of sauna and confessional.

What was good enough for the Apaches was good enough for the Wannabes, and they had constructed their own sweat lodge out on the plains. It was built to the exact and authentic design of the original Apache sweat lodges, with the authentic hemispherical shape and the authentic doorway facing east. The sweat lodge was covered (I happened to notice) with authentic black PVC garbage bags, perhaps the very same authentic black PVC bags that the Apache had used to take out their garbage (take it out to where?) or perhaps not. Anyway, Dick took me aside in order to prepare me for my Ordeal by Sweat.

He explained that I was going to be reborn. (This was a bit of a problem, since my mother apparently had a fair amount of trouble with it last time, and I wasn't sure she was ready for another go now.) I would leave behind me all evidence of my present life. (Even more of a worry, since this included my nice leather jacket and my new wristwatch. But perhaps I wouldn't need them in my new life. Or perhaps I could trust those who remained outside with my old life to look after these Holy Relics for me.) I would enter from the east, meditate and chant (nothing too difficult there), and then emerge reborn. Just like that. It was similar to the Primal Scream form of therapy where you delve back into your past to your first scream at birth and start all over again from there. Only this was obviously more of a Primal Sweat. I was ready for it.

I kept my underpants on. This was partly because – as the university don said when he covered his face when surprised sunbathing nude on the riverbank by the ladies' rowing eight – most people recognise me by my face, not by my downbelows. And it was partly because I know that young starlets' careers can be ruined by nude shots being published after they've made their name as a serious actress (not, of course, that I was considering a career as a serious actress, nor that I was a young starlet, come to that). And partly because I realised this film would be seen all over the world and I was keen to advertise the very best products of the Marks and Spencer underwear department. And partly too because I have a tattoo on my left buttock that reads 'I LOVE THE

B.B.C.', a relic from my early days in radio when I thought that demonstrable loyalty would enhance my job prospects.

All these thoughts flashed (as it were) into my mind as I stood in the sleet at minus five degrees and immediately flashed out again to be replaced by another thought, i.e. 'Get out of the cold and into the warm or you will die.' With something between a Primal Whimper and a Primal Shiver, I rushed (from the east) into the dark and hot tent, and the flap was closed behind me.

The glow of the red-hot coals illuminated a little circle of about twelve naked Wannabes. They were sitting politely round the fire like a fondue party at which somebody had unaccountably stolen everyone's clothes – and the fondue. The leader of the group, a slightly older woman (I noticed), welcomed me and told me not to be afraid (of suffocation rather than nudity, I assumed). They would start chanting, and if I felt like joining in, I could. The chant was a little unintelligible to me (it sounded like, 'Oh, Eagle! I welcome you in!' or perhaps it was 'Oh, Eagle-eye! Welcome in!'). All the while, the Wannabes sat in the dark and nude, and they sweated together, occasionally combing the sweat off each other in the caring and sensitive manner of cave baboons. That was all just fine and dandy, but the major problem was the air. There wasn't any. I suppose it was like a sauna, but I've never been in one of

Primal whimper
The author bares his soul (and much else) on re-emerging into his old life after the sweat lodge.

those, so I'm not used to the sport of recreational suffocation. I was having difficulty getting the oxygen to my brain and was on the verge of recreational hypoxia. If this was meant to be my rebirth, then, as a re-foetus, I felt it was about time my re-obstetrician got me out so that I didn't get rebirth brain trauma. But I didn't want to appear a coward in front of all these kind, brave and nude persons, so I stayed on.

Then, just as I was beginning to get used to it, the leader threw a ladle of water on to the hot stones so that instead of breathing pure scalding hot air we were now breathing pure scalding steam. I was *definitely* ready to be reborn out of there right now. Gasping for air, I thanked the nude assemblage and, muttering a prayer to my re-womb to give me a good push to relaunch me into the world, I symbolically raised the flap of the tent and rushed out. I have never before – or since – been glad to be in the snow in my underpants. The air was lovely, even at minus five. I quickly re-invested myself in the relics of my Old Life (particularly my Old Life's New Wristwatch) and took stock of the situation.

I had certainly had a revelation of sorts. As a result of my experience, I had definitely decided that being born once is quite enough for any normal human being. People who want to repeat the process frequently are, as the saying goes, in danger of becoming the suckers who are born every minute. I knew then that I definitely didn't wannabe a Wannabe, so we thanked them kindly and moseyed off back to the Old Life.

8

CHICAGO:

Whose Kind of Town?

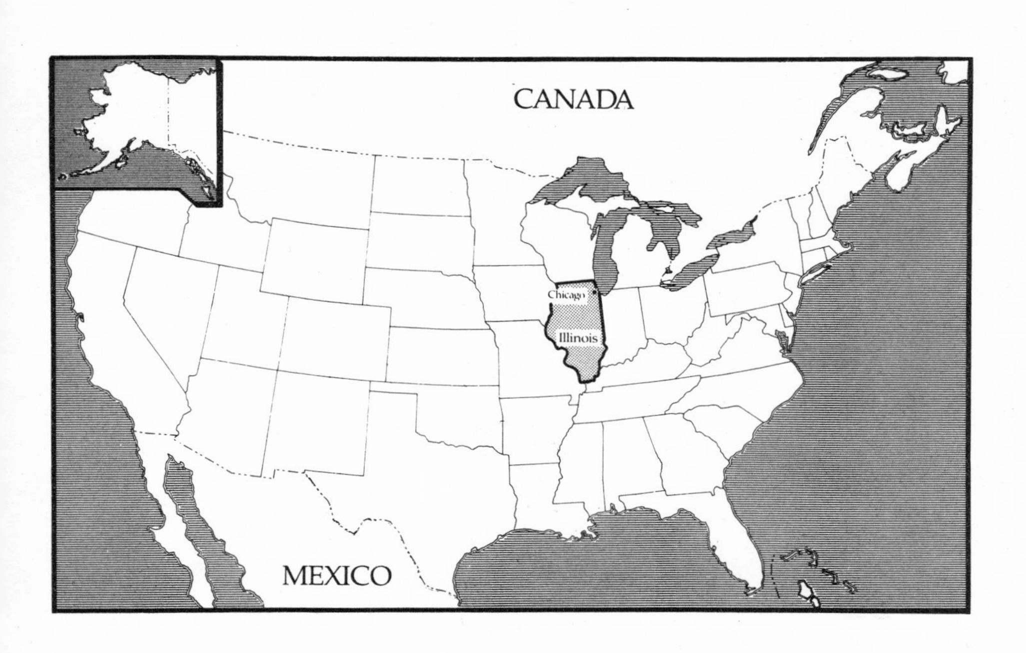

God, Guns and Guts Made America Great – Let's Keep All Three: Murder and Mayhem in Cook County Hospital

I'm sorry, but this piece is not going to have anything funny in it. While we were in Chicago we spent a Saturday night in the largest and busiest hospital trauma unit in the city – the one at Cook County Hospital. What I saw there sickened me. In my career I have seen a lot of death and major trauma and I am no longer squeamish when I am involved in the care of somebody with serious injuries. That was not what sickened me in Chicago. What disturbed me – and continues to disturb me as I write this – is the total profligacy of it all, the waste of human life for no reason whatever. The American fascination with guns is, in my view, the most obscene and perverted aspect of the American dream. It is built on illusions of personal freedom and self-defence, and it is fed on commercial profit, dreams of self-aggrandisement and the equating of violence with achievement and social status. It demeans the American way of life and, for about 25,000 Americans each year, ends it. It is a lethal absurdity, simultaneously revolting and pointless. It is as stupid as the bumper sticker from which I took my title: 'God, guns and guts made America great – let's keep all three'. If only they could see Cook County on a Saturday.

It was a slow night by Cook County standards. The humidity outside was not very high, and that meant there wouldn't be a large number of shootings. Humidity and violent crime are linked so closely that you can plot a graph and predict the number of shootings with uncanny accuracy. In the summer, when the humidity climbs into the eighties there may be thirty or more victims of violent crime in a weekend. During the Saturday night that we spent on the Trauma Unit, the humidity was below forty, and the team only had to deal with two shootings, two stabbings and a head injury from a blunt instrument. A slow night by Cook County standards.

The Trauma Unit didn't look very dramatic or very busy. In well-organised hospitals it's the emergency department, not the trauma unit, that swarms with the city's walking wounded. The emergency department is the one that features in all the movies. The flotsam and jetsam of the neighbourhood flood in and make their demands; some are mad, some are sick, some are both, and many are not ill at all but want somewhere warm to sit down and a sympathetic ear for their troubles. In the movies, the seriously injured are rushed through the emergency department on stretchers, pushed by frantic orderlies and trailed by doctors shouting orders at attractive nurses who hold up intravenous drip bottles. The Trauma Unit of Cook County was one step away from all that. The flotsam and the jetsam had been filtered out downstairs, and only the major injuries were transferred to the second floor. Although this gave the unit an air of relative calm, it meant that every case that did come through the wooden swing door was a serious one.

That night, the charge nurse in charge of the Trauma Unit was Jose. Jose was a slim, slight, attractive woman in her thirties and carried with her an aura of authoritative calm and an unruffled sense of capability and responsibility. If there was a fire, she would be the person you would want to stand next to. She had been on the unit for several years, and it would take a lot to surprise her.

The first patient that came in on the evening shift was (by Chicago standards) nothing special. He was fifteen years old and he had a .22 bullet in his head. The X-ray showed it very clearly, lodged behind the fleshy part of his nose, about an inch away from the front of his brain. The two residents (the American term for what we call 'registrars' – doctors in training, in this case for a career in orthopaedics) went over to talk to him; he was conscious and free of pain but very frightened. He gave his name as Freddy and he was black. The vast majority of the Trauma Unit's patients were either black or Hispanic. In fact, the statistics show that if you are a black youth in Chicago your chances of being shot before the age of twenty are one in twelve. That's not an easy

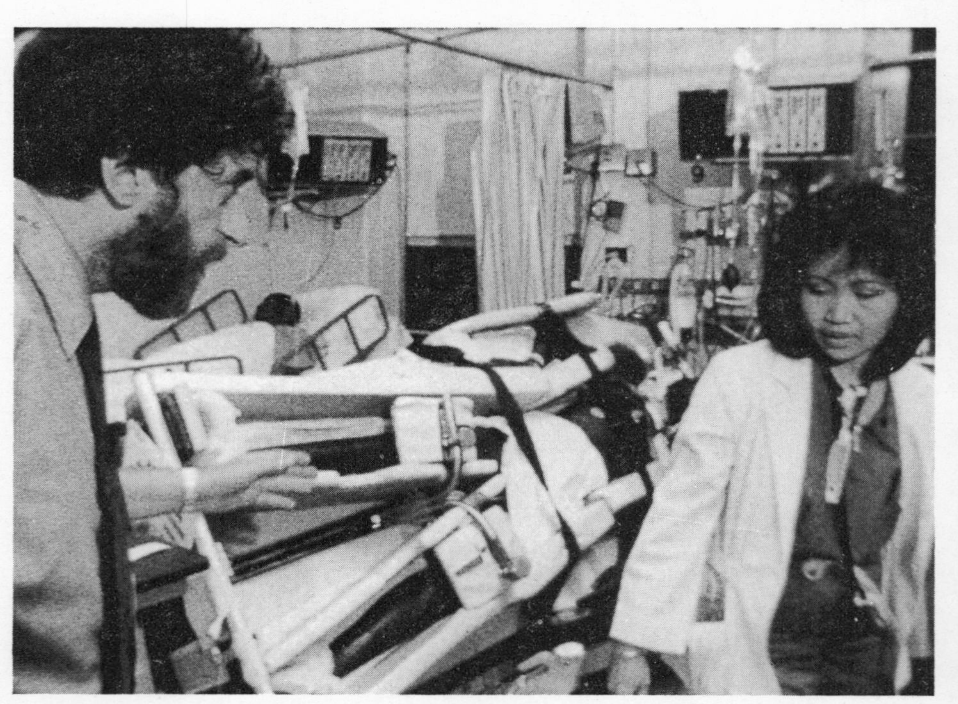

In command
Nurse Jose keeps her cool while all about her are losing theirs.

statistic to assimilate – think how you would feel if your child was going on a trip and had a one-in-twelve chance of coming back with a twisted ankle. That alone would be worrying enough; perhaps it would even cause you to keep him or her at home and cancel the trip. But we aren't speaking of something as trivial as a twisted ankle, we are speaking of being shot, and this isn't any trip that can be cancelled – this is life in Chicago, and you can't keep your children away from it.

According to Dr John Barrett, the Irish orthopaedic surgeon who ran the unit, the great majority of the patients were members of local gangs, and most shootings were the results of vendettas and you-got-one-of-ours-so-we'll-get-one-of-yours feuds. What they usually told Dr Barrett was that they were standing on the street when somebody shot at them. Sometimes some of the relatives told the medical team that they knew who did it but that there was no necessity to call the police. They wouldn't press charges, they would sort it out themselves, and the person who did it would be brought into the unit within the next couple of days. Freddy told the residents what happened. He was standing on the street, and somebody shot at him. The two residents tried not to look bored and blasé, but in the Trauma Unit that line was about as original as 'my wife doesn't understand me' or 'our cheque is in the mail'.

Freddy hadn't seen where the shot had come from, but he had felt it hit his tooth. The bullet had bounced off his tooth and ricocheted upwards behind his lip, before tunnelling backwards into the soft part of his nose and coming to rest underneath the cartilage – mercifully in front of his maxillary bone. There was no bony injury, and there were no splinters of bone that could do damage. He had lost very little blood, and his facial skin and soft tissues were intact. Whoever fired the bullet was an inch away from being a murderer. You could call it luck, although I suppose Freddy would only have called it luck if the bullet had missed him altogether. The residents organised the removal of the bullet. Freddy would be on his way home in a day or so.

Suddenly there was a kerfuffle in the next bay. A man in his thirties had been stabbed in the chest. The wound was in his right side, towards the back, and he needed a few tests to make sure that there was no serious injury to the lung, pleura (the coverings of the lungs) or liver. The noise and struggle were caused by the patient. Without being an expert on the subject, I could tell fairly quickly that he had been taking drugs. He was talking gibberish most of the time and was virtually incoherent. The only thing that was clear was that he wanted to go home right then. He was not prepared to wait for an X-ray, for a blood test or for an assessment by a thoracic surgeon. He wanted out of there. And he was prepared to make a fuss and insult the nurses and doctors until he got his way. His demands were not negotiable. He got his way.

The next two hours were quiet. Jose took advantage of the relative peace to show me round the rest of the ward, where patients recovered after surgery or waited for placement or convalescence. There were a dozen or so beds, and the ward was very clean and well run. Most of the patients had suffered major injuries which had been repaired. Their lives were no longer in danger, but they had nowhere to go. The most tragic patient in the ward was in the most expensive bed. He was strapped into an electric miracle that every few minutes turned from side to side so that the patient's skin would be protected from pressure sores. His legs were strapped into the limbs of the Y-shape of the lower end of the bed, and his top end was connected to a ventilator which did his breathing for him and which meant that he couldn't talk. Before his admission to hospital he had been a taxi driver. Somebody had decided to rob him for the few dollars in the cab, and in the process of the robbery had decided to shoot him. The bullet had penetrated the spinal cord in the cervical region, paralysing the poor man and ensuring that the rest of his life would be spent silently on the expensive rotating bed in Cook County. If the emergency care at Cook County had been less than perfect, he might have died straight away, and if the long-term nursing care were less effective he might have died of pressure sores or respiratory problems. But, on the other hand, if small-time robbers weren't able to buy guns across the counter perhaps he would still be earning his living in his taxi. I suppose the thoughts that were going through my mind would no longer have made any impression on Jose. Violent crime, as far as Cook County hospital is concerned, is like the weather: it's what there is outside. My thoughts would have seemed to the Trauma Unit as pointless an intellectual exercise as sitting on a beach in the south of France wondering why the sky was blue all the time. I tried to disguise my own feeling of depression at this clean, tidy ward full of sad and resigned victims, but I couldn't think of anything to say. However, my own silence was brief – there was a new admission and Jose was needed urgently.

It was a case for neurosurgery. A man in his sixties had been brought in from another hospital. He was found in deep coma at his home and rushed to the local emergency department, where a CT scan of his brain showed that something (or somebody) had hit his head and caused bleeding inside the skull on the outside of the brain – a situation known as an extra-dural haematoma. The blood from the ruptured blood vessel had accumulated outside the dura, the tough covering of the brain, and the pressure from the accumulated blood was squeezing his brain, causing the coma. The situation was now a surgical emergency. He was unresponsive to any stimulation, all his tendon reflexes were absent, and none of his limbs moved even by reflex action when stimulated. Unless the pressure was relieved at once he would die in minutes. This was certainly a situation I had seen before in Britain, and I had seen similar patients rushed into operating theatres and operated on. But I had never seen it dealt with on an open ward with such speed and dexterity. Before we were even aware of it, the neurosurgeon, Dr Ghandi, was in the Trauma Unit assessing the CT scan and the comatose patient. Within minutes, he was gloved and ready. The right side of the patient's scalp was quickly shaved, and Dr Ghandi performed a burr-hole. In essence, this meant that a hole was drilled into the skull above the haematoma and the blood was drained. It was over in a matter of minutes. There were six people around the bedside, and we waited. This time there was a happy ending. After a few minutes the patient's left foot moved when the toenail was squeezed, and after another few minutes the same thing happened on the right. He began to move his upper limbs when stimulated. He would recover. However, nobody would ever find out what happened to him, and when he recovered consciousness he wouldn't be able to remember events immediately before the injury either. For all concerned, perhaps that was for the best.

The next patient was Gregory. Gregory was older than Freddy. Whereas Freddy was just a kid of fifteen, Gregory was a young adult of sixteen. This time the bullet was a .38, and it was in his right leg. I joined the residents as they examined his leg. While they were looking at his

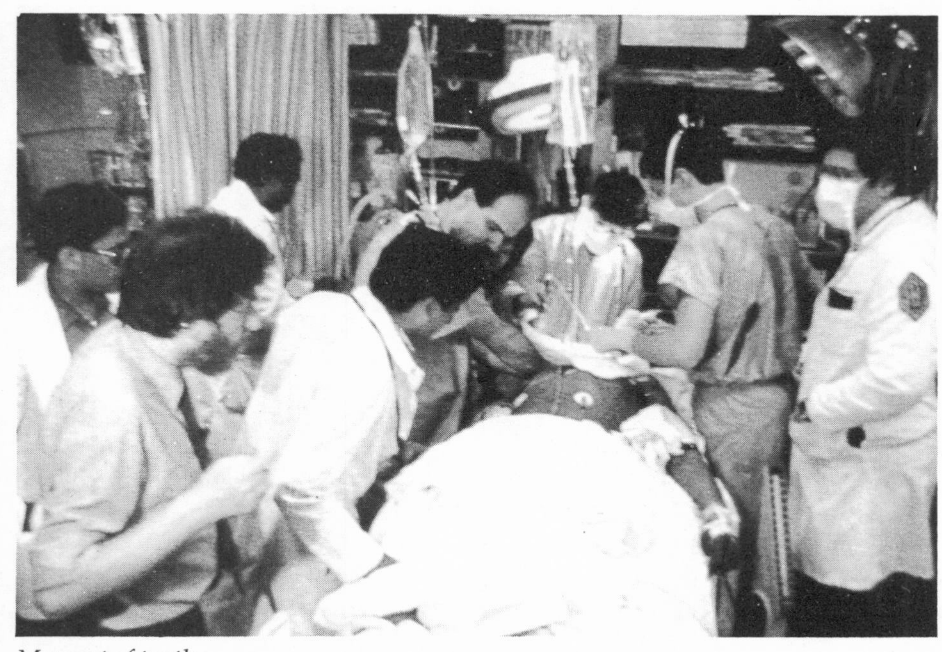

Moment of truth
Dr Ghandi evacuates a large blood clot pressing on the patient's brain while everyone else waits for any movement of the patient's limbs.

wound, I asked Gregory what had happened (which marks me out as a novice in the neighbourhood). Gregory said he was standing on the street when somebody shot at him. The bullet had entered his right leg just below the kneecap. It must have been going relatively slowly when it had hit, because it had made a small entry wound, then tumbled over before ending up on the other side of his leg pointing backwards towards the entry wound. With Gregory's permission, I felt the bullet under the skin. It was lying just beneath the skin and was easy to locate. It so happened that I had never felt a bullet that was fired in anger before, and the first thing that struck me was that it was much bigger than I would have guessed. If somebody were to pick up a .38 bullet and simply throw it at you, it would hurt like hell. Fired from a gun, the damage that it might cause suddenly meant something. The residents were very relieved that the position of the bullet relative to the entry wound meant that there was little chance of any serious damage to Gregory's leg. I suppose it was lucky – but, like Freddy, Gregory might have had other ideas about what constitutes luck. I was beginning to think that Chicago was only an exciting city to certain people, and that those people were not the ones coming through the door of the Trauma Unit.

When I spoke to Dr Barrett about what we'd seen, he showed a

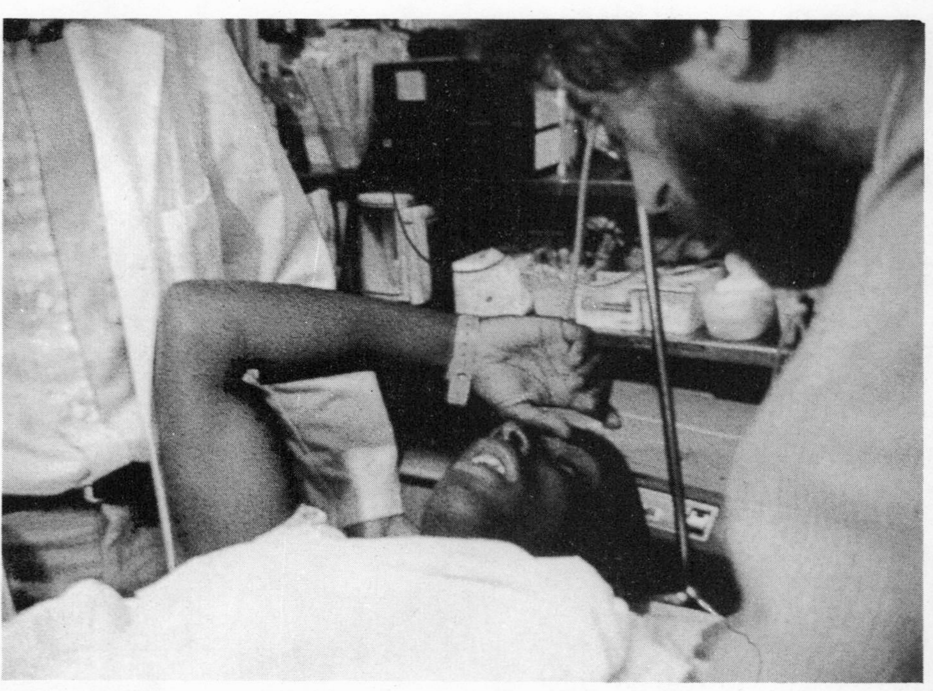

Where it hurts

Gregory tells me about the gunshot wound in his leg.

remarkably philosophical attitude. He was born and trained in Ireland; he emigrated before the recent troubles and he told me that, before coming to Chicago, in his whole medical career he had only seen one gunshot injury. This was a farmer who had accidentally shot himself in the foot with his shotgun. That kind of accident doesn't happen in Chicago. John Barrett seemed to have two main attitudes to what was going on around him. On the one hand, there was a never-ending stream of seriously injured people who needed surgical repairs ('They haven't invented a pill yet that will fix a gunshot wound'). On the other hand, he knew that most of this human misery was avoidable and that gun control might reduce it. John had spent a lot of time campaigning for gun control laws, but he was not hopeful. Despite the widespread advertising by the National Rifle Association against gun control laws (adverts which feature sportsmen with rifles on duck shoots), it needs to be said clearly that handguns are not used for shooting birds, game or deer. You use rifles for all those. The only target for a handgun is a human. At present, there are three million handguns in Chicago – three million anti-human handguns. John did not think that in ten years from now his services could be dispensed with. On the other hand, one must be thankful for small mercies. With only two gunshot wounds, two stabbings and a head injury, it really had been a slow night. By Cook County standards.

Postscript

Looking back at what I felt, it occurs to me that any American who reads this chapter would wonder why I was making so much fuss. No one died that night, and no one was even paralysed. And in some respects it might seem extraordinarily over-sensitive of me to become so upset. After all, I had seen many worse injuries in Britain – in road accidents, industrial injuries, domestic accidents and so on. But the thing that upset me could only upset someone who wasn't born in America; it was the pointlessness of it all. This wasn't some war in which like-minded men group together to carry forward their ideals (whether misguided or not) by major force of arms when all else has failed. This was a gratuitous escalation of aggression. The guns are freely available over the counter. So if somebody feels like robbing a store or a taxi driver or feels like being the Big Kid on the Block, he buys a gun to support his argument. And so many people buy guns to facilitate their greed or desire for status that sooner or later everyone else thinks they have to have a gun to defend themselves. And when the humidity rises, tempers shorten and the guns settle arguments that would otherwise have come to a few blows or insults.

The average 'God, guns and guts' style of American cannot easily imagine a society without free access to guns. People brought up in other societies cannot imagine why the Americans persist in this pointless destruction.

Here are two facts which may help get a perspective. On the border that runs between Canada and the United States, there are two towns separated by a bridge. On the Canadian side, the town of Windsor had 8 killings by gunshot in 1987. On the United States side, Detroit had 1,542. The only thing that separates the two communities is a bridge – and the difference between American and Canadian attitudes to guns.

Here is another fact. One argument in favour of guns is that honest upright citizens need to have guns in order to defend their families and homes. In 1986 a survey was carried out on 398 gunshot killings which happened inside homes in King County, near Seattle. Of these 398 killings, only two were shootings of an intruder. For the record, 41 were criminal murders, 7 were self-defence murders during an argument, 12 were accidents and 333 were suicides. This means that, if an American keeps a gun in the house for 'protection against criminals', if that gun goes off and kills someone there is a 99.5 per cent chance that the dead person will be the homeowner or a member of the family. What would the average consumer say about a mousetrap that had a 99.5 per cent chance of killing the householder and not the mouse? Something definitely made America great. It may have been guts, it may possibly have been God, but it certainly wasn't guns.

9

ARIZONA:

Where Everything Sticks, Stings or Stinks

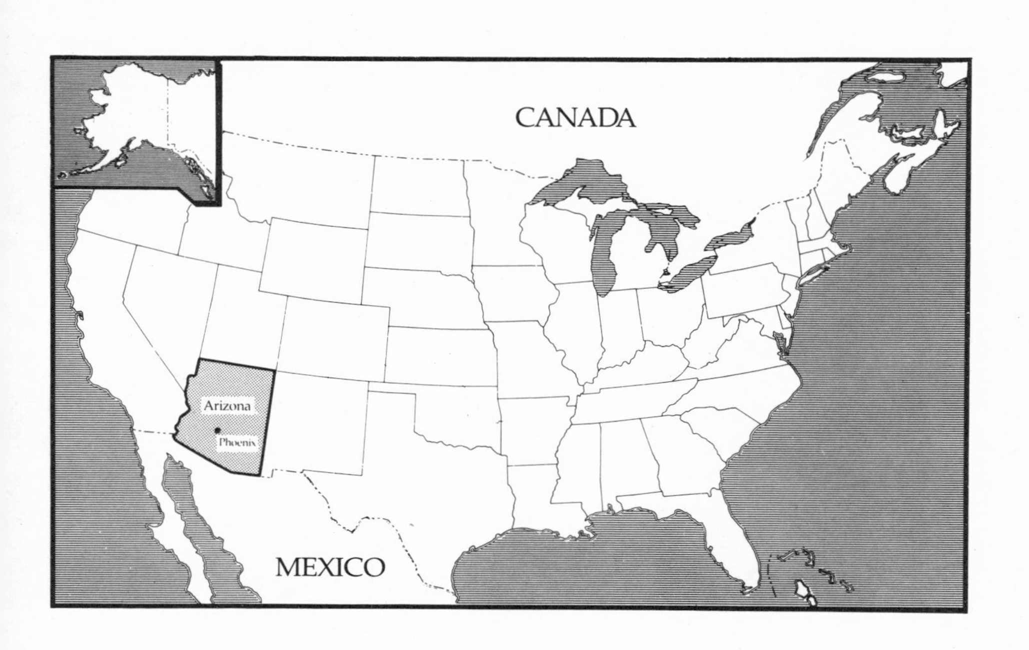

Just Deserts:
Lorin D. Honitschlager Leads a Desert Safari

In their incessant restlessness, the Americans have made great inroads into almost every wild area of their continent. The Arizona desert is no exception. It is an incredibly hostile and inhospitable environment, but it is attractive to the older Americans because it is warm in the winter. As a result of new immigration, the poor desert is being nibbled away at the edges by a spreading suburbia. Few of the new occupants really know anything about the desert itself, and few care. I met one of the exceptions.

We learned about Phoenix's renowned Deadly Scorpion Hunter from a most respectable source. The University of Arizona is the licensed producer of scorpion anti-venom, a serum which each year saves dozens of young children and adults from the painful and possibly fatal consequences of scorpion stings. Of the twenty-six species of scorpion in Arizona, only the bark scorpion is potentially lethal, and the university team raises the anti-serum by injecting small doses of this scorpion's venom into goats. This means that they need a steady supply of scorpion venom. Which in turn means that someone has to go out into the desert and collect a large number of these lethal scorpions and ask them please would they kindly donate their venom to the University of Arizona thank you very much and you get a cup of tea afterwards. The name of the man who herds up the scorpions and turns them into generous venom donors is, we were told, Lorin D. Honitschlager. It surprised us that he wasn't Lorin D. Honitschlager III or Lorin D. Honitschlager Jr. Just plain Lorin D. Honitschlager. Well, not plain really – he was listed as Lorin D. Honitschlager, Deadly Scorpion Hunter, and it was clear that this was the one person anybody interested in the scorpion game ought to see. We made an appointment.

Meeting Lorin for the first time is like opening a cupboard and having four brooms and a bucket fall on your head. His way of greeting people with a jovial embrace could get him two years for grievous bodily harm where I come from. He is a bear of a man with a brown, crinkly weatherbeaten face and a repertoire of expletives which could embarrass any four navies of the world. 'Hey, how the **** are you? Let's have a ****ing beer!' as he took us to the bottom of his garden where he had lovingly constructed his very own tiny bar, complete with saloon-type doors. 'I can drink here, I can even ****ing sleep here if I've had a spat with my wife. She knows where I am and sometimes I do too.' His laugh was a proper old-fashioned roar, and he was free with it. His house was at the edge of one of the interminable suburbs of Phoenix, which is a

The deadly scorpion hunter in his lair

messy sprawl of a city, a vast puddle of one-storey houses covering zillions of square miles of desert for no particular reason and with no particular place to go. In the midst of this drab and aimless uniformity, Lorin's house was at least individual. The garden had a reconstruction of a gold mine and two stuffed rattlesnakes on pneumatic piston arms that leapt out when anyone walked past. Inside the house there were several of Lorin's children, a few of their respective spouses and a smattering of grandchildren. Plus Lorin's long-suffering and happy wife, and the parrot. It was a wonderfully noisy crowd, and there was a great deal of toing and froing, including, I seem to remember, my doing my W. C. Fields impression, which went down very well though I can't remember why. The parrot was an exceptionally active participant in the conversation and broke in with 'Polly wanna cracker', 'Hi!' and a very dirty laugh. While Lorin and the gang were out preparing the truck, I became convinced that the parrot must have picked up a lot of Lorin's swear words, so I stood in front of the cage and tried a few of his favourite expletives to see if there was any response. At which point Lorin came back in and wanted to know why I was using bad language and swearing right in front of the ****ing parrot. I didn't have a very good explanation, so I did some more W. C. Fields impressions to change the subject. We saddled up the old jeep and moseyed out of town.

The only advantage in Phoenix, particularly at the edge of it, is that you don't have to go very far to get into the desert. Within twenty minutes' drive we had left civilisation behind us (if you can call Phoenix civilisation, which you cannot) and were in the desert. It was late afternoon, and the shadows of the tall saguaro cacti were already beginning to lengthen as the desert started to cool. As we followed a trail into the hills, Lorin grew lyrical about the natural beauty of the desert years ago, and then bemoaned what was happening to it now. Matching his words, the scenery began to change, and we saw garbage, detritus, effluvia and the flotsam of civilisation scattered around us – in short, the litter that America creates when left to itself. It began with portable litter (wax cartons, soft drink cans and paper bags) filling up the gullies and sticking to the cacti like bills on a spike. Higher up there was the heavier stuff. There were car bodies turned upside down like dead turtles, sofas bleeding their horsehair stuffing on to the ground, sodden old mattresses and undescribable shapeless mounds of grey stuff that had once been something else, probably even less attractive. And everywhere there was evidence of America's fascination with guns. Every object that would show a dent or a hole when shot at had been used for target practice. Car bodies, bottles, cans and saguaros alike were all riddled with hundreds of bullet holes. One can have no idea how depressing it looked – the beautiful desert littered with this random vandalised crap.

Lorin told me that less than two miles away there was an indoor shooting range where anybody could fire away to their heart's content in isolation and safety. But the locals didn't want to go to the expense of paying for the shooting range so they vandalised the desert instead. The admission fee for the shooting range was one dollar.

Lorin had a fascinating moral tale. A few years before, one target-practising maniac had aimed at a saguaro of about sixteen feet in height. It had been standing there for about three hundred years, but the maniac had decided that it was now fair game. As sometimes happens, the centre of this particular cactus had rotted through, with the interesting result that when the maniac fired at it, it broke in half, and three tons of cactus fell straight on top of him, killing him instantly. His friend took the story back to town, and Lorin said that very few tears were shed.

By now we had climbed above the litter belt and were into real proper desert. We dismounted and started our search for the bark scorpion. I must admit that I wasn't really scared, but a little apprehensive. As I have already told you, I don't have a Thing about Snakes – it's one of the few features that distinguishes between me and Indiana Jones. He does have a Thing about Snakes. But I didn't know whether I had a Thing about Scorpions or not. Lorin started stepping warily around the bushes and rocks, so I did my kimo-sabe trusted-Indian-guide stuff and followed in his footsteps. Apparently scorpions live under rocks, and the trick is to turn a likely rock over quickly and grab the scorpion with long tweezers before it runs away. Part of the art is to work out which rocks are small enough to be flipped over, and my first choice was a rock which was still very much part of the mountain, causing me to detach my retinas with the strain. Following Lorin up and down, we soon had our first hit. It was a big fat scorpion about two inches long, with a dark brown tail at the back end and very visible pincers at the front. My first reaction was not fear but revulsion. The most unpleasant aspect of a scorpion is that it doesn't seem to have any eyes. In fact, it doesn't really seem to have a face of any description, and one is a little dubious about whether what is at the front end is actually a head.

I have a major theory that mankind is frightened by things that don't look and move like humans. We can come to terms, in a way, with anything with a proper face, a pair of eyes and an even number of legs (preferably between two and four). But when things don't seem to have eyes and move funny (such as spiders and crabs) we shy away from them even if they are not dangerous. This may be the reason that snakes don't bother me – unless I know they are poisonous; they have eyes, and even though they move funny, at least it makes some sort of sense. Scorpions are like automated moving cactus twigs. They are coloured a sort of pasty translucent brown, like something that comes from the

Crazed by success, the author tries to outstare the captured scorpion (which is difficult since the scorpion has no eyes).

effluent pipe of a plastics factory. And they are peculiarly hairy. They have little stubs of hair at intervals down their bodies, which makes them look rude and gross. And, in addition to all that, they don't look at you (because they don't seem to have eyes), so they seem to be moving like one of those wind-up toys that dart about randomly to astonish your friends and amuse your family – sixty pee each, three for a quid. Anyway, this was our first hit, so we nabbed it with the tweezers and put it into a large Tupperware container. Lorin had furnished the inside of the Tupperware with cardboard compartments so that his prisoners shouldn't kill and eat each other (which is one of the major personality flaws of your average scorpion). I explained that in England we would ensure that this did not happen by sending in Lord Longford to visit the prisoners every few weeks.

It was still a bit too warm for the scorpions to be out in large numbers, so we made slow progress over the hill. Then Lorin found a big round hole in the ground and announced with considerable pride that it was a tarantula hole. He started enlarging the hole and probing it with a stick to find out which direction it pointed in. I watched in mild alarm. I was fairly certain that I didn't have a Thing about ordinary spiders, but since I had never met a tarantula (except the green plastic ones on elastic that my kids think will astonish me and amuse their friends, etc.) I wasn't sure whether or not I had a Thing about Tarantulas. So I asked Lorin about them. At this point he had his entire right arm in the tarantula's hole up to the elbow, with his face close to the ground. 'A tarantula bite ain't bad,' he assured me. 'It ain't got much venom. It just bites you – you know, like someone sticks a ****ing dinner fork in your hand and twists it round. But no venom.' I asked what bite (on his scale of good to bad) *would* be classified as 'bad', if being stabbed with a dinner fork wasn't. A bite from a tiger perhaps. Lorin thought that was a valid viewpoint, but didn't think it was very likely that there would be that many tigers lurking at the bottom of a tarantula hole, so he dismissed my cautions. He dug on for a few minutes, but it seemed that Mrs Tarantula wasn't at home to visitors. Lorin's theory was she was out hunting for prey, but my theory was that she didn't want to appear on television. (I could just imagine the lady tarantula at the bottom of that hole telling her kids 'Being nabbed by a Honitschlager ain't that bad. You just get this huge hand round you and you're supposed to stick your dinner fork in it. The real problem is, once you've been on the telly, everybody recognises you, and bang goes peace and quiet. So we'll just sit here till the old bugger's gone.') In any event, there was no human–tarantula contact. So, with some disappointment at not having the opportunity of being stabbed by a dinner fork, Lorin stopped his excavations, and we moved on.

By now dusk was doing its fully professional number. The sight was more beautiful than I could have imagined. It inspired me, and when it comes to landscapes I don't inspire easy. A deep red glow lit the far hills, and below it, in their shadow, the valley filled up with a lovely warm liquid purple. It was such an extraordinary colour, and it seemed so luxurious and almost tangible, that we all just wanted to go on looking at it. It was an addictive colour, and we were hooked.

We wanted a shot of Lorin walking across the skyline in the beautiful dusk, and he happily set off to the next hill. At this point we couldn't see him very well; so once the camera was lined up, Dunstan shouted out, 'Lorin, could you walk a bit further to your right?' He explained the situation graphically, and his words shattered the calm of dusk. 'Not unless I walk right into this ****ing rock, I can't.' 'Fine,' said Dunstan. We got the shot, and the sun sank further behind the mountains. We all fell silent as the shadows thickened and deepened. The immensity of nature and the transient puniness of mankind impressed themselves upon us. And in the peace and solitude of that magic moment, some berk up the mountain started rifle practice, and someone else echoed with a few bursts of automatic fire. The locals were saving a dollar.

In the desert, everything really gets going at night. During the day almost all of the animals hide in their burrows or under rocks and do nothing except sneer at the tourists. Then, as soon as it gets dark, all the animals sneak out, looking for prey. Since every predator is someone else's prey, this produces a potential frenzy of after-dark pairing-off like a deadly wife-swapping party. The scorpions, beastly creatures that they are, do not miss out. But, unknown to them, they have a chemical in their skin that shines brightly under fluorescent light, which enables man, including the Deadly Scorpion Hunter, to track them easily in the dark. Lorin switched on his little ultraviolet lamp. Sure enough, as we edged along the hill, there were a half-dozen scorpions of various sizes glowing an astonishingly bright fluorescent green as they moved about in their peculiar way. It was like a desert disco. Now Lorin was in his element, and we zipped around for another hour or so until he thought the Tupperware prison had got its quota. We saddled up and returned to base.

By now it was about nine o'clock, which in the Honitschlager household is milking time for the scorpions. The bark scorpion does not yield its venom easily (unless it's stinging you). In fact, it requires nothing less than an electric shock to persuade the little rascal to donate. Lorin's set-up for the scorpion milking was less like a milking shed than a movie-set torture chamber. His daughter Julie did most of the milking because, Lorin explained, it's actually ****ing delicate work and she's better at it. Julie wore thick rubber gloves and held each scorpion tail-upwards under a magnifying glass near a little glass tube leading to a tiny bottle. She then applied a pair of fine tweezers to the tail, and with

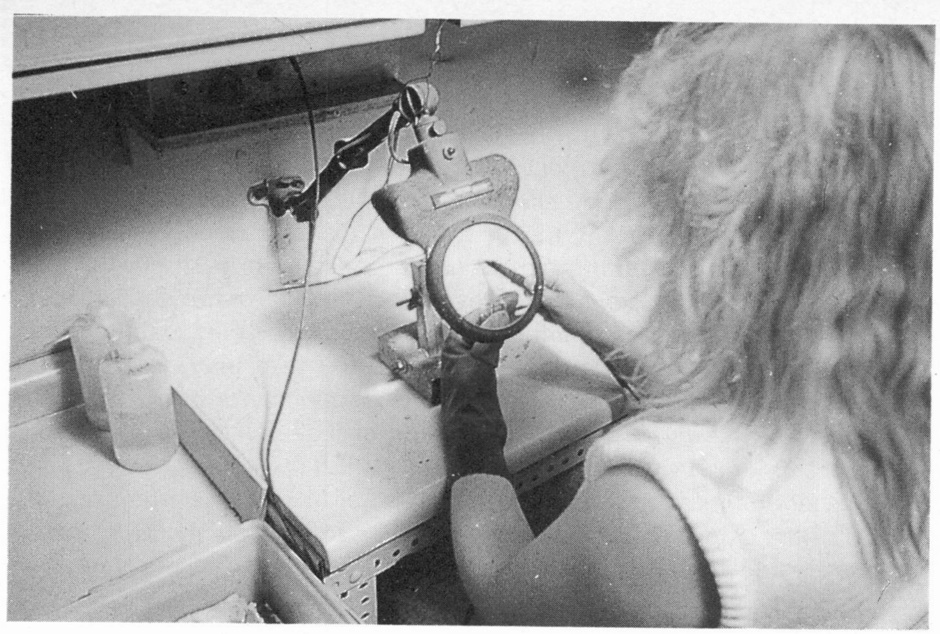

A tail of two sittings
A kindly and generous scorpion willingly donates its second drop of venom when gently prompted by the Deadly Scorpion Hunter's daughter and her persuasive electric forceps.

a foot pedal passed a small electric current through the tweezers. The shock caused the scorpion to part with its venom, and a tiny bead of fluid, less than a pinhead, went into the tube. After two or three dozen of the little blighters had been milked there was a visible collection of venom about the size of a medium-sized raindrop. A pint of scorpion milk would require approximately two million animals. Apparently some scorpions are 'good milkers', and some aren't. In any event, each one gets milked once a week, but after a few weeks they can't produce any more because of the long-term effects of the electricity. I wanted to know what happened to them after they'd given their all and could no longer produce. Were they, perhaps, turned out to stud with free grazing, a generous pension and the thanks of a grateful nation? No. They were sold to the scorpion equivalent of the knacker's yard. In fact, milkless scorpions end up embedded in perspex as paperweights and key rings, so if you ever buy such a thing (and I hope you don't) it's of some comfort to know that the animal inside has at least made its contribution to society. It may seem a little mean jolting the hell out of a poor dumb animal with painful tweezers – but, when you think about it, they'd do it to us if they could. And when they can, they do.

St Geoffrey of the Desert: The Man from Harrogate Finds Peace

The Americans do not have a monopoly on eccentricity. The English invented it as a lifestyle, and virtually patented it centuries ago at a time when New York was a city of two wigwams. (Or is the correct plural wigswam?) In those days, eccentricity had a certain intrinsic charm and fascination. It travelled with the Pilgrim Fathers on the 'Mayflower', and was one of our most successful invisible exports. It was noted and half-admired by later generations of the settlers of the New World, and until a few years ago an English accent in America automatically earned the bearer an aura of charm, a certain status and a measure of tolerance for any eccentric habits. Nowadays, the value of the English lifestyle has been somewhat devalued against the dollar, and every well-spoken Englishman has to earn his aura of quaintness and charm instead of inheriting it automatically. This is a little more difficult if you happen to be an Englishman making a stand against the juggernaut progress of The American Way. Geoffrey Platts – a hermit by profession – is an English crusader in Arizona.

We were sworn to secrecy. The exact location of the desert home of Geoffrey Platts, the Hermit from Harrogate, is strictly confidential. All that I can tell you is that it is somewhere in the Arizona desert and is situated in a tiny valley thirteen miles from the nearest village. Although this narrows it down a bit, your chance of finding it on this information alone has been calculated as precisely zero to eleven decimal places. Actually, nothing will help you find him, not even explicit instructions from *him* as to how to find him. Working on the painstakingly detailed directions and map that Geoffrey had sent us, Dunstan and I still managed to get totally lost. Mind you, it has to be said that both of us lack any viable sense of direction whatsoever. Dunstan couldn't find his way out of his bath if the taps weren't there as a landmark, and I've managed to get lost trying to get out of a telephone kiosk. As a result of this marriage of true impediments, we spent nearly three hours blundering about in the desert, accidentally exploring hundreds of little ravines and dusty dry hills. Eventually, however, by the laws of statistical randomness, we found ourselves at the top of a little dirt track that matched Geoffrey's description, we found the secret key to the locked gate just where he said he had hidden it and we moved on down.

All that I knew about Geoffrey was that he was an emigrant from Harrogate and was a staunch defender of the desert in the old English stop-the-motorway-coming-through-our-village style. I had read a few newspaper stories of his protests and demonstrations, and a strange image had floated into my mind. I was reminded of another English eccentric environmentalist called Commander Bill Boakes, who used to stand for Parliament every general election for the Homes before Roads Party or something similar. Boakes used to appear on the TV to ginger up any pre-election dull moments and was a grizzled, slightly intimidating old man with the intense but vacant stare of the full-blown pedigree nutter. Even Robin Day used to have a tough time interviewing Boakes, and I wondered if Geoffrey was going to be Harrogate's export version of the same thing. As we drove down the track, I therefore prepared myself to meet a true hermit. I imagined that without electricity and running water he would look somewhat shaggy. I imagined a white beard and tattered clothes like Robinson Crusoe's before he did his designer goatskin number. I prepared myself for an onslaught of antisocial behaviour, antisocial appearances and antisocial smells.

The reality was even more bizarre. At the bottom of the track a gentle stream trickled through a wooded valley a few hundred yards long. Shaded by dozens of trees and by its steep rock walls, the valley itself was cool and quiet. Outside the valley, the Arizona desert was the film set for *A Fistful of Dollars*. Inside the valley walls, we could have been in a backwater of Maidenhead or Richmond. I half-expected to hear the distant sounds of the Henley Regatta. On the opposite bank of the little stream Geoffrey's shack was also a little unexpected. It should have been a proper desert shack like the ones you see in cartoons. You know the kind, they're made of three planks nailed together, and have two vultures sitting on the top. This desert shack looked like a large garden shed on someone's country estate. It was a tidy wooden single-room hut about twenty feet square. In front of it, a clearing, with a table and rudimentary brick fireplace set into the hillside, served as dining room and kitchen. Mentally I tried to write a London estate agent's listing of the property for a quick sale: 'Desert country home; one recep, K & B outside, frnt gdn, no grge, no H & C, no TV, no elctry, no neighbrs, no road, not close tube/train/bus. Architectural features: roof, walls. Close to desert, easy access desert and more desert. Ideal for no-family eccentric hermit.'

After being battered within an inch of my life by the effusive greetings of Lorin Honitschlager, meeting Geoffrey was a culture shock – although a few days in Arizona had undoubtedly lowered my threshold for feeling shocked, particularly by culture. It was instantly apparent that Geoffrey was nothing if not cultured. A tidy man waved at us in the typical half-embarrassed pleasant manner of the country gentleman. ('Hello! Glad you found the place. Come on up! I've just got some coffee on the go.') No white beard, no shaggy rotting clothes, no vacant staring; instead here was a man looking to be in his mid-forties, hair neatly brushed, moustache neatly trimmed, shirt neatly ironed and shorts neatly pressed. The perfect model of an insurance broker on his weekend off (assuming that there are insurance brokers who spend their weekends off living in secret valleys in the middle of the Arizona desert). And he did have coffee on the go, maturing on the brick fireplace in a blackened stew-pot obviously borrowed from the props department of *Rawhide*. The coffee, as Geoffrey explained, was *café de rancheros*, a thick black highly caffeinated concoction made by boiling chopped coffee beans in springwater until they part with every last molecule of their best poison. I know I shouldn't, but I judge a man by the colour of his coffee. Coffee, as far as I'm concerned, is not exactly an addiction, more an obsession. Anyone who serves decaffeinated dish-water or thin tin-flavoured instant bilge is immediately labelled a Baddy and consigned to the same section of my mind that already holds the Moonies, Attila the Hun and herpes. Geoffrey scored ten out of ten for his coffee, and another ten out of ten for not having antisocial clothes, manners or smells. I thought I could like this man.

As we started talking, I found myself liking him more and more. His history was a peculiar one. By his own confession he had been a bit of a Jack-the-lad in his youth. He had misspent a lot of it, hanging about in bars in Harrogate, drinking and womanising. Nowadays he could probably have got an Arts Council grant to finance his lifestyle as an innovative art form, but in those days it was just dismissed as laziness.

Oasis
Geoffrey Platts' Thames-valley country estate in the middle of the Arizona desert.

He failed to complete his university degree, so I suppose he was a fifties prototype version of a drop-out. I'm not sure what they called drop-outs (or is it *drops-out*?) before the sixties; I think it might have been 'work-shy bastards'. Anyway, Geoffrey was stuck with no degree, no known skills or talents and three years' experience of drinking and womanising. In my opinion, this would have qualified him for a brilliant career in advertising or politics, but in 1958 nobody asked me for my opinion (I was ten at the time), so Geoffrey decided to emigrate. The only job offer that seemed remotely interesting was from a hotel in Arizona.

At that point the major direction of Geoffrey's life could be best expressed in a single word: 'directionless'. He had no idea of where he was going although he was quite eager to explore a few options, and he worked five months a year to finance some serious jaunting in the other seven. He visited Japan and taught English, and he paddled up the Amazon River in a dugout – neither of which were average activities for the times. He then settled down in this particular bit of Arizona (which I will not name, not that it would help you even if I did) and came to love the desert and to resent the way that mindless and aimless expansion of the cities was cutting into it. His real moment of truth came a little later in (appropriately) Paradise Valley, which was silting up with bottles, plastic bags and tins, and was rapidly turning from Paradise Valley into Hell's Wastepaper Basket. It was the litter that gave Geoffrey his road-to-Damascus vision. He got Involved. He organised a major anti-litter campaign which was an extraordinary success (although the bottles and plastic stuff started creeping back in later).

And from that moment on, he progressed towards leading the kind of life that would preserve the kind of world in which it would be possible to continue leading that kind of life. He was not a natural-born crusader, but gradually a central idea took shape in his mind that seemed to sum up his view of the world outside and of himself inside. 'The answer is to reduce one's needs,' as he put it, and this concept made sense to him at two levels. If mankind (specifically American mankind) could learn to want less (in the way of golf courses, condominiums and freeways) the depredation of the desert might stop. And what goes for mankind also goes for man; Geoffrey quoted Carlos Castenada (who was Very Big in the sixties): 'What makes us unhappy is to want. Yet if we would learn to cut our wants to nothing, the smallest thing we'd get would be a true gift.' In practice, Geoffrey is exceptionally good at reducing his needs. Each year he goes on a solo hike into the desert with the express object of avoiding all human contact and living off the contents of one back-pack and anything else he can find. It renews his love of the Sonoran desert and reminds him that he needs to keep his needs down.

Now, many of us might agree with this idea of reducing our needs *in theory* and we might nod sympathetically with a 'Yes, yes wouldn't it be a better world if we were all less greedy and wasteful and didn't drop litter or kill the whales, and perhaps while we're at it we could all beat our swords into ploughshares and lie down with the lamb, etc. etc.' But even for those of us who support the principle, translating conscience into a change in behaviour has never been a popular pastime – particularly in Arizona. I mean, let's be frank, Arizona in the sixties and seventies was not exactly the world centre of altruistic sophistication. It was not then (and is not now) the sort of place where you would be rewarded for your selflessness and dedication to your fellow humans, or where you could survive if, like a Greek or Chinese philosopher, you wandered about the place doing your philosophising and relying on alms from the locals.

So Geoffrey became, literally, a prophet without honour in his own land (wherein, as they say, honour is more normally accorded to profits, rather than to prophets). But, as he reminded himself, 'Philosophy provides only peace of mind, freedom and tranquillity, not worldly riches or external power.'* Arizona, being a well-known centre of worldly riches and external power, sent a clear message to Geoffrey: if you wish to change the world, you will have a major fight on your hands, buddy. And so he entered an escalating ecological crusade which gradually took over his life and eventually shaped it.

He became a one-man pressure group. A few miles down the road, they built six golf courses so that Americans would be able to play golf in the warm all the year round. Each golf course needed a million gallons of water a day to keep the greens green. What that does to the environment and the water table under the sand nobody can tell. Even a desert needs a tiny bit of water, and if the golf courses take that, it could be catastrophic. So Geoffrey wrote letters to the papers. He stood outside corporate buildings with placards (in temperatures over 100°F). He churned out protests (all in his own handwriting, an unmistakable italic calligraphy, which I bet the local councillors are now allergic to), sending up to two hundred letters a week. He took on issue after issue. He campaigned for laws covering non-refundable bottles and managed to force a referendum on it (which was lost) and fought for a plant protection regulation for one region (which was won). Bit by bit, site by site, he fought the good fight for the desert and became, as he put it, 'the voice for the voiceless'.

During all this he lived – as he still does – as basic a human existence as is possible. His current lifestyle is like that of those little birds that live on hippopotamuses and clean their skin, doing a little bit of good and absolutely no harm. He doesn't have a car (which means it takes him nearly two hours to walk to the nearest mailbox, but then his respiration

*Epictetus (AD 60–120).

More kicks than pricks
Geoffrey Platts comes to grips with the cacti.

doesn't pollute the atmosphere as much as a Chevrolet does, and he doesn't burn fossil fuels). He washes himself in the stream. He picks up litter wherever he goes (and persuades anybody who is driving into town – including Dunstan and me – to drop off a full bag of it) and recycles everything that can possibly be recycled; he burns old telephone directories in his woodstove. To buy the things he cannot pick, catch or grow, he does wonderfully dramatic readings from his own writings (mostly about his solo hikes) or other Great Stuff (e.g. Edgar Allan Poe). The audiences love it, and he sells out every time at five bucks a head.

We only spent a few hours together but we covered a lot of ground. I was left with the impression of a man who had led a long and successful campaign for personal peace. His small hut showed it. It was as tidy and neat as he was: rows of books (D. H. Lawrence, Henry Thoreau, Herman Hesse), tidy piles of journals and magazines, and a few neat and tidy Things. It was a really peaceful and uncluttered place to live.

Geoffrey had a lot in common with Buddhist philosophy ('The first half of one's life is spent in the cut-and-thrust of experience, and the second half in contemplation'). I imagined that it had not always been a simple campaign – none of the Human Urges release their hold easily – but he had achieved a genuine and stable balance with himself and with the world around him. I envied him that. Although I'm still wading through the first half of life and very much into worldly riches and external power (of which NHS doctors have remarkably little), I envied Geoffrey his peace. Perhaps I'm not quite ready for a major war against my own Urges yet, but even so, there is something about the way Geoffrey is leading his life that makes me want to go back some time and visit him. If I can ever find him again.

10

PHILADELPHIA:

The Cradle of Democracy

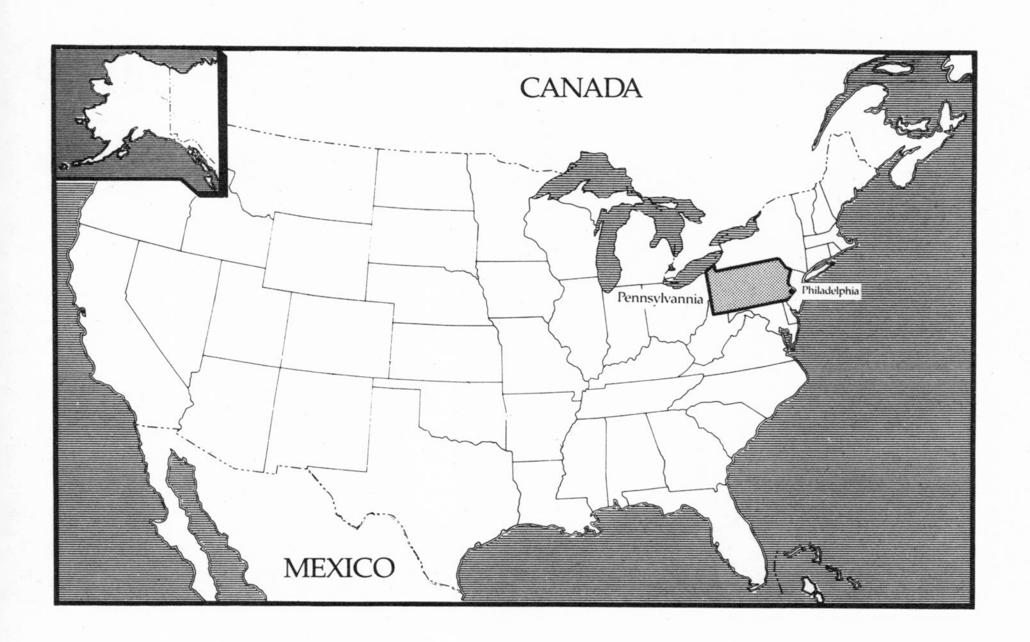

Auf Wiedersehen, Pet:
What the Philadelphians Do for Their Animals and Vice Versa

Human beings interact with animals in thousands of different ways, many of them quite legal. Sometimes those interactions benefit the humans without benefiting the animal (e.g. bacon); sometimes it's the other way round (e.g. tapeworm). Sometimes the interaction seems to benefit neither (for instance, when a mosquito bites me, I kill it with DDT and the evening is spoiled for both of us). However, there is one thing we do with animals that they never do with us – that is, keep them as pets. The habit of keeping pets (defined as domesticated animals that do not provide food or produce) may go back to our cave-dwelling ancestors, and there is now some evidence showing that keeping pets may enhance the pet-keeper's health. Naturally, in America if there is even a hint of health enhancement, there will be specialists trying to study it and promote it. And other specialists to cope with any adverse consequences.

I am often asked what my favourite animal is. Usually I reply, 'Smoked salmon.' This may betray a rather hazy grasp of the role of animals on earth, or it may equally well betray a callousness for the plight of those poor salmon who each year have to smoke themselves to death for our benefit. Or is that kippers? Anyway, apart from the fact that I enjoy eating the cooked carcasses of deceased animals, I happen to get on well with living ones. I like them, and they usually like me. At cocktail parties, I seem to be the natural target of the hostess's dog, who spends most of the evening sitting with me and licking me (when, quite often, none of the human guests will do either of these things). I like cats and budgerigars, I love taking my kids to the zoo, I support the restrictions on whaling, I mourn the extinction of forest fauna and I'm sure that had I been born in the last century I would have dropped a groat or two into the tin for the 'Save the Dodo' fund. But I don't think of animals in quite the same way as I think of humans.

I am not without experience in this area. Our favourite cat (whom I christened 'Rover' because I didn't want it to grow up with Fixed Attitudes) was a sweetie-pie, but she was still only a cat. We also had a dog. The dog was a male, and very visibly so, but was named 'Jenny' by my daughter (who was then three years old, and whose dog Jenny was supposed to be) despite vast bribes to change her mind and thus save us adults the embarrassment of calling out, 'Jenny, here boy!' to an obviously male dog in the park. Jenny was a terrific and energetic dog. He was fun, he was enthusiastic and he was nice to throw sticks for when there wasn't anybody to talk to, but he wasn't anything more than a dog. On the other hand, he wasn't anything less than a dog, which is also important. I thought of him as a pet, and as a constant source of enjoyment, fun and stuff you step into accidentally in the garden. I never thought of him as a form of medical treatment or health enhancement. I now realise that this was an oversight on my part, and that Jenny was almost as good for my health as a high-fibre diet (though, to be honest, neither he nor I had any problems in that direction).

I remember reading, a few years ago, of some interesting research work done in a coronary care unit looking at groups of people recovering from heart attacks. The research team looked at various groups of patients with varying severity of heart attacks and tried to discover what factors affected the speed and the degree of recovery. Obviously the size and the extent of the heart attack were of major importance; but within groups of patients with the same severity of heart attack, one of the major factors affecting recovery was whether or not the patient kept a pet at home. If you are the kind of person who keeps a pet at home, it seems you are the kind of person who will do a bit better after a heart attack. It occurred to me at the time that there must be a minus side to this obvious plus. For instance, if Person A keeps a dog and thus does well after his heart attack, how do we know he isn't damaging the health of his neighbour Person B who has a tidiness obsession and high blood pressure and gets even higher blood pressure every time he inadvertently steps in the excreta of the dog of Person A, particularly if Person A is in hospital and not able to participate fully in the dog owners' stoop-and-scoop programme? However, these are trivial quibbles. The research work sounded very much in the mainline of The American Way, so we all trooped off to Philadelphia to find out more.

The City of Brotherly Love has clearly extended the definition of 'brother' to include members of other species, following the example set by its School of Veterinary Medicine. The University of Pennsylvania is known as plain 'Penn' – and they get upset if you confuse it (as I did) with 'the state pen', which means the federal prison. At Penn's School of Veterinary Medicine, Dr Alan Beck is director of the Center for the Interaction of Animals and Society. Now, in the States a great many academic posts are sponsored by beneficent industrial giants, who endow named professorial chairs. This means that one is constantly meeting people who are called things like the *'Nelson D. Rockefeller Professor of Genetics and Inherited Wealth'* or the *'Betty Crocker Cakemix Professor of Low Molecular Weight Carbohydrate Metabolism and Shortbread Recipes'* or the *'Diet Pepsi and Orange Fanta Associate Professor of Transmucosal Gas Diffusion and Burping'*, etc.*

*Just in case any of those mentioned are telephoning their lawyers right now, these are hypothetical examples and do *not* indicate the existence of any such professor whether alive or half-dead.

It occurred to me that Dr Beck's would have made the perfect sponsored academic appointment: the '*Colonel Sanders Kentucky Fried Chicken Party Bucket Professor of the Interaction of Animals and Society with a Choice of Coleslaw or Frenchfries*'.* But no, Alan Beck turned out to be a straight academic and one who takes his work, but not himself, seriously. We found him in his laboratory on the sixth floor of the Penn Small Animals Hospital. Actually it so happens that I have never visited a veterinary hospital before, and I was surprised by how much it resembles a real hospital – oops, I mean a hospital for humans (sorry, my Fixed Attitudes are showing). The waiting rooms looked just like humans' waiting rooms except that there were steel loops on the wall so that the patients' leashes could be tied and untied easily. I also noticed that when animals sit in a hospital waiting room they, like humans, can only read copies of *National Geographic* that are at least three years old. The clientele was fairly representative of the US pet population. Apparently 60 per cent of American homes contain pets, of which number approximately 45 per cent are dogs and 30 per cent are cats, with caged birds making up 10 per cent. I'm not sure what the remaining 15 per cent are – presumably the odd turtle, a polecat or two, a few monkeys and miscellaneous invertebrates, e.g. tapeworms, mosquitoes, smoked salmon, etc.

We gently picked our way through the quiet and well-behaved throng of patient dogs and cats and slightly less patient (but still quite pleasant) humans that they had brought with them, and found our way up to Dr Beck's empire. I found Alan Beck distinctly (to use the Italian word) *simpatico*. As one might have hoped of a Professor of Pets, he had the personality of a teddy bear. He was kindly and humorous and, although distinctly learned and expert, he managed to avoid displaying either of the cardinal sins of pomposity or rock-hard salesmanship. His research work is detailed and labour intensive. Basically he has been studying the biological and psychological effects of owning and handling pets, using physical and psychological methods of assessment. In a typical experiment he will put blood pressure monitors on to a volunteer and measure his or her pulse rate and blood pressure before, during and after interaction with a pet. Simultaneously, the session will be video-recorded, and the body language of the volunteer will be studied by Beck and the psychiatrist with whom he collaborates – Dr Katcher (is that an appropriate name for a man who studies dogs or what?). It was the Beck/Katcher team who showed that groups of psychiatric patients benefited from interactions with (please try not to giggle when I tell you) finches. In their research, Beck and Katcher showed that those groups of patients who had finches in their therapy room recorded better

*See footnote on page 144

attendance, better participation and less hostility than those groups of patients who didn't get the finches. You can make what you will of that, but I must say that although it sounds a bit silly it does make a fair bit of sense when you think about it.

Anyway, this is what Dr Beck does in real life, and we sat in on his afternoon session. His first volunteer was Nicole, who is herself studying to be a vet. Nicole settled in and was strapped up to the monitors. Some pre-petting readings were taken, and her body language was video-taped. Speaking of body language, I think it is only fair to point out that Nicole was, as it happens, an extremely attractive young woman. I didn't notice this myself partly because I am a professional doctor and broadcaster and am trained to ignore such things, but mainly because I am married. However, the film crew – many of whom are unmarried, or claim to be while in a foreign country – obviously noticed that Nicole was an attractive young woman with great body language, and it was a great shame that Dr Beck didn't have the blood pressure and pulse monitors on them. I am sure that he would have observed better participation and less hostility from a film crew in a room with Nicole than a similar crew in a room without Nicole. However, Nicole was not interested in the film crew (very few sane people are); she was only interested in her pet, a parrot called Thai. Or perhaps it was Tie. I'm not sure because he never signed his name or gave a calling card (apart from the usual calling card of birds, which he left with casual nonchalance on the top of the video monitor). Anyway, Thai was brought in and settled on top of Nicole's shoulder while she carried on talking to Dr Beck.

Dr Beck asked Nicole about how she talked to Thai, and asked her to talk to him while she was being observed. It was fascinating. As she turned to talk to the parrot, she dropped her voice to a soft, low, rather sexy croon. Thai bent his head towards her mouth, and they each did a little pouty kiss – which was extremely difficult for Thai since he didn't have any lips, but to his everlasting credit he had a good try at puckering up his beak. It was a tender moment. Beck's monitors showed the effect. Sure enough, Nicole's blood pressure and pulse rate went down. Beck explained to her that during her interaction with Thai all her body language and voice tones were becoming gentler and softer (something the film crew had noticed without the benefit of a medical education). He explained that for the human participant this was a substitute for a 'kiss-and-cuddle' interaction, but from the parrot's point of view it was a substitute for a grooming session. Now, this must have been perplexing to poor old Thai. Nicole was clearly getting all the nuzzling she needed from him, but if Dr Beck was right, then Thai wasn't getting the goods as promised from her. He must have been very disappointed that Nicole wasn't pulling any nits out of his feathers or getting the wax out of his

Heavy petting
Thai, the parrot, takes a break from staring down the front of Nicole's dress.

ears or whatever it is that parrots do to each other when they groom. On the other hand, Thai certainly didn't *look* disappointed, although it's not easy to tell anything from a parrot's facial expressions (which is why you should never play poker with a parrot). Anyway, while Dr Beck engaged Nicole's attention on the subject of interaction, Thai sat on her shoulder, ignoring the doctor totally and devoting all his energies to looking down the front of Nicole's dress. There was no doubt about it; Thai cocked his head on to one side and stuck one beady eye, and then the other, straight down the front of Nicole's dress, looking up occasionally to make sure nobody was watching him, but not stopping what he was doing when he realised I was. Sadly, Beck's monitors weren't recording Thai's blood pressure, but you didn't need to be a vet to tell that he was extremely happy thank you very much. It was clearly more fun than having nits pulled out of your feathers. But all good things must come to an end, and after another few minutes of mutual benefit Nicole and Thai had to move on.

Beck explained to me what had been going on. 'Birds are especially comforting because they are more vocal than dogs and cats. Almost any sound made by the bird is sufficient to stimulate dialogue from the owner, which creates companionship, and companionship is soothing' – clearly to both parties. 'Bird owners use more sounds and play with speech more than dog owners. Birds may be a better stimulus for this kind of soothing "baby talk" than dogs.' I could believe that. And I could also believe that Thai would believe it, too. In fact, I could easily imagine that Thai would give a strikingly similar account of his afternoon to any other parrot he met. ('It's a very pleasant way to spend the afternoon, Joey-boy; all you have to do is say a couple of "roo-koo-koos" and she'll let you look down her dress for half an hour. She probably finds it very soothing. Actually she seems to like it so much, I'm thinking of going freelance next year. Got to look out for Number One, Joey-boy.')

As somebody once said a long time ago, it doesn't matter what you do at home provided it isn't so loud that it frightens the horses. With Nicole out of the way, the film crew (who had been watching Thai's voyeurism with considerable interest and a modicum of envy) simmered down. They stopped all their tapping of the side of the nose with the forefinger, nudge nudge wink wink, and repeating of the words 'heavy petting' and 'oh-ho-ho', and they got ready for the next bit. The next bit was to be me.

By now I know when a 'surprise' is on the way. Dunstan starts simpering and trying not to giggle, and there are sidelong glances and silent nods. Clearly something was afoot. I tried to be grown-up about it and sat down while Dr Beck (who was clearly in on it too, whatever it was) hitched me up to the monitors. Once my pre-sessional recordings were done, another student brought in the pet that they'd lined up for me to interact with. It came in a large stout hold-all and it was a boa constrictor. He was about six feet long and weighed about fifteen pounds, and his name was Billy. They gave me the head end first, and draped the rest of him over my shoulders. Now, in our business – particularly with bounders like Dunstan on the loose – you have to expect the unexpected. I was expecting something that was supposed to scare me, and I was damned if I was going to be scared. However, after our experience with Nicole and Thai, it did occur to me that perhaps this snake might also try to look down the front of my clothing and maybe even slither down under my shirt to all stations south. This was a pretty bizarre thought and so redolent of Freudian overtones that I immediately decided not to think it any more. My next thought was even more bizarre. It was, 'This is nice.' But, to be honest, it *was* nice.

If you have never held a snake you don't have any idea of how nice it can be. Snakes are covered in pure 100 per cent snakeskin, which when it is on a handbag feels hard and crackly, but when it is on a snake feels smooth and silky. The scales all point backwards, and it felt very comforting to be stroking the skin from head to tail (what am I saying here?). The other thing that was good fun was the way Billy moved about. He must have measured about five inches in diameter, and most

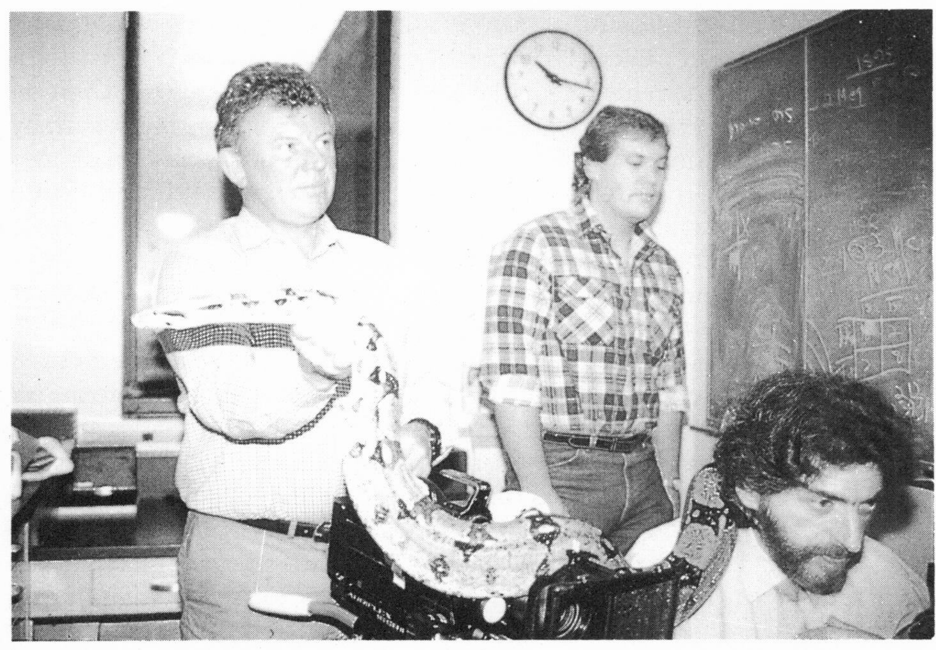

Mighty Flynn
Chas Flynn (director) attempts to direct the business end of Billy (convincingly portraying a young and bewildered boa constrictor in this film).

of it was muscle. The waves of muscle contraction could be felt moving up and down his body, which was also quite soothing. Communication was, I have to admit, somewhat limited – to 'Who's a pretty boy, then?' on my part, and to slithering on Billy's. It was difficult to know what to do to please him. You know where you are with cats; you just tickle them under the chin, and if they like you they nuzzle closer and purr. Billy did none of these things. For a start, there was no chin for me to tickle him under, so I had to stroke the top of his head. Secondly, he didn't purr. In fact, he didn't do anything very much apart from slithering. No, that's not quite true, he did stick his tongue in and out a lot, which was something to go on, but it wasn't exactly like being licked by a puppy. So, although I was having a bit of fun stroking his snakeskin outfit, there was simply no way of telling whether he was having fun or not. He simply wandered about the place in a seemingly random fashion, apparently ignoring all human intervention.

While I was talking to Dr Beck and being comforted by Billy's skin, Billy himself simply moved on. His head end slithered over my arm, on to the table, over Dr Beck and on to the film camera. At one stage I was caressing his tail end while his head end was draped so tightly over the lens that the cameraman couldn't adjust the focus. Having investigated the camera with his flicking tongue, Billy obviously missed the comforting contact with a human and promptly wrapped himself around the nearest available substitute for a human being, our cameraman Mostafa. I still don't know whether Mostafa has a Thing about Snakes, but it was clear that this particular snake had a Thing about Cameramen. Personally I think it was a match made in heaven, but that may have been a little unfair to Billy. In any event, the point was proven. My pulse and blood pressure went down during my contact with Billy, and another interaction of Animals with Society had concluded beneficially – although Billy may have had some reservations about any Society of which Mostafa and I are thought to be representatives. However, there was no time for a major sociological discussion with a snake, so we said goodbye to Billy, crammed him back into his hold-all and moved on.

Saying goodbye to a pet isn't always as easy as that, as our next visit demonstrated.

In my professional life, I have often helped to support the surviving relatives of someone who has died as they go through the process of grieving after their bereavement. On many occasions I've also witnessed the benefit that relatives gain from group therapy. The shared experiences of other people help the survivors to regain insight and perspective, and to feel less isolated and abnormal in their grief. But, of course, I've only seen that when the person who has died was both a family member and a human being; it never occurred to me that the same process would be as intense if the 'family member' was a pet. But in Philadelphia, pets are taken so seriously that the grief suffered by a bereaved pet owner merits every assistance, including group therapy.

Each Thursday evening, on the ground floor of the Small Animals Hospital, a group therapy session convened of which all the members had lost a much-loved pet and needed help to cope with their grief. We watched through a one-way mirror (with, of course, the knowledge and consent of the group) as they shared their experiences and their sadness. There was no doubt of the intensity of their feelings. One woman said, 'My girlfriend killed herself, but it wasn't the same. She was my girlfriend: I wasn't with her twenty-four hours a day. I was with my pet twenty-four hours a day.' Another group member compared the death of her pet with the death of her father: 'I found the death of the animal was harder. The death of a pet is cleaner, not as complicated and much, much sadder. Animals are innocent. My father wasn't innocent.' Another couple had lost a dog, and the wife cried deeply and uncontrollably for the whole of the group session. Listening to her grief one would never have known that she was speaking of her dog and not a member of her family: 'He was so sick . . . he was yellow . . . We decided that when the quality of life went away we should not keep him alive. He had nothing left at that point. They couldn't get the IV in . . . His liver was beyond repair, and he was anaemic. He was real sick, so we did the right thing for him. It just hurts so much.' And the group shared the intensity of her pain.

So what should one make of this grief and its therapy? On the one hand, it would be very easy to dismiss it all as a lot of self-indulgent Americanism – a group of neurotics with nothing better to do than to wallow in uncontrolled emotions that may actually have been encouraged or even incited and created by the atmosphere of the group. When one stands on the opposite side of the one-way mirror, that is a comfortable attitude to take. These people seem to be overdoing it, to be going 'over the top'. It's all a sign of inadequate personalities, of insecurities, of neurosis, of Americanitis and so on.

But there's another side, and crossing the barrier by stepping out from behind the one-way mirror and going into the room with them brings out that other side. These people are in pain because they have lost the target of much of their love. That target happened to be an animal, not a child or a spouse, but that does not necessarily negate the value of the love that the humans expressed. At some level, that love has value and has worth. I don't happen to think that love for an animal is as valuable as love for a human being, because the exchange is so asymmetrical as to be almost one-way, and the love involves less growth, less true tolerance and less true understanding than a love for a complex human being. But that's just my opinion. If these people were congregating to mourn, say, the loss of their jewellery or the dividends on their stocks, I *would* feel that the emotions shown were inappropriate and unhealthy, but the loss of a pet is a loss of a loving exchanging relationship, and it hurts.

In the end, the value of the process is the value of what is put into it. Some of the mourners were clearly able to use their experience to move on, to progress, to become (for want of a more defined word) better. For them, the experience was useful and important, no matter whether it was the loss of a human or an animal. For others, the experience was another in a series of swamping, overwhelming misfortunes that had always haunted their lives. They would fail to cope with this in the same way that they had failed to cope with the past ones.

Finally, it all boils down, not to a laughable Americanism, nor to a chest-beating social ritual, but simply to the fact that grief is a lesson. And the value of a lesson depends on what is learned, not on who the teacher is. The only difference between America and Britain on that score is that they seem to have more kinds of lessons, and feel less embarrassed about going to school together.

Not Very Deep Throat: Dr Robert Sataloff Looks a Bit Down in the Mouth

Performing arts medicine is undoubtedly the new thing for the ambitious doctor at the leading edge of medicine in the United States. Nowadays so many people make a highly successful living by the art of performing that there is plenty of room in the world for a few doctors to make an equally successful living by helping those performers keep making theirs. One enclave of this rare breed of medic is the Arts Medical Center, which offers Professional Voice Care. It was there that I took my professional voice to get it cared for.

This was another of Dunstan's hare-brained schemes. He'd found out about this very high-tech doctor in Philadelphia who had two zillion dollars' worth of gleaming and blinking electronic equipment which could measure all the intimate intricacies and foibles of the human voice. What's good enough for Luciano Pavarotti, according to Dunstan, would be good enough for us. Meaning me. What he actually meant, but did not say, was that the good Voice Doctor had a whole lot of expensive gleaming and blinking equipment that he shoved down people's throats; and that the intimate views of your hero's glottal crevices plus the incredible discomfort that would be caused thereby would make exciting television. But I wasn't told that last bit. Until afterwards, when I knew all about it and didn't need to be told.

Now, I am the first to admit that I like the sound of my own voice. Like it? Hell, I love it because I live off it. But I don't love it so much that I want to look at it. I knew, from my medical school days, that the voice came from somewhere called the vocal cords. I vaguely remembered that they lived in the dark somewhere behind the tongue and below the waggly bit at the back of the throat which we doctors technically call 'the waggly bit at the back of the throat'. And that, I thought, was all I *needed* to know about where my voice came from. It was certainly all I *wanted* to know.

The offices of the Arts Medical Center were very swish. Not the usual American Swish with pink marble everywhere and everything either plated in gold or covered in wild silk, but proper European Swish. The walls were panelled in a lovely oak; there were comfy leather armchairs, nice old fireplaces and Proper Old Pictures on the walls from the Victorian era when Proper Painters did pictures that were so good that you recognise the place they were meant to be. Those were the days, and now these were the offices. However, the comfortable surroundings were not meant merely to impress the incoming would-be Pavarottis (or is the correct plural *Pavarotti*? I suspect that Pavarotti, like scissors, is already a plural – he certainly looks like that – in which case the singular should be *Pavarotto*. Or to be more accurate, since he is not a small person, *Pavarottono*. Sorry, I shouldn't have started this). Anyway, the plush surroundings were not intended merely to impress the incoming opera singers, they were also designed to reassure them – just like the typical fish tank in the dentist's waiting room. Actually, even the fish tank trick can backfire; I have a friend who developed inverse Pavlovian conditioning, and every time he saw a goldfish or a guppy got a terrible pain in his wisdom teeth. However, the lovely panelled and comfortable offices were clearly meant to give any nervous potential patient a sense of solidity, trust, comfort, faith, positive thinking, relaxation, calm and tranquillity. All of which would vanish instantly the moment the Voice Doctor shoved his zillion dollars of gleaming torture instrument down their throats. But that was ahead of us. Or rather, me.

Dr Robert Sataloff is everything a specialist for opera singers ought to be. He is intelligent, charming, witty and smooth. He is also something that opera singers find particularly reassuring, i.e. he is an opera singer. Not a pretend opera singer or a bathtub baritone, but a real opera singer – the kind that sings foreign stuff with a choir on a stage in front of people who have paid money to listen. Like most baritones, he is not a small person, but he is astonishingly quick in his speech and movements and gives an aura of speed and energy which is quite common among American doctors who work in private practice. However, unlike the typical American upper-crust doctor who is really a businessman with a licence to draw blood, Robert Sataloff is an enthusiast and an academic. He simply loves his subject. He loves singing, he loves the human voice, he loves the science of studying the faults of the larynx, he loves setting them right and, it has to be said, he loves shoving gleaming instruments down people's throats. But, as I said earlier, that came later.

First, there was the easy stuff. Robert introduced me to his lovely voice therapist and research associate, Linda. Linda was so lovely that if you saw her on the arm of (say) a Sylvester Stallone and he said, 'This is Linda, my voice therapist', you would nod knowingly and say to yourself, 'Oh, yes, THAT kind of voice therapist.' In fact, Linda was once nominated in a Miss America contest, and my personal theory is that she was disqualified because they found out she had an IQ of 140. Anyway, her beauty contest days behind her and her colleagues far more refined than movie stars, Linda is a highly skilled voice technologist and, like Robert, has an infectious enthusiasm for her subject. She settled me down in her basement laboratory and connected me up with a microphone and a wallfull of electronics. Her fingers darted nimbly over the control panels of a few thousand dollars' worth of gadgetry, and she told me to say 'Aaah' for as long as I could. I did my very best, but the result was most disappointing. At least, Linda was pretty disappointed, which meant that I was pretty disappointed, too. Despite my own illusions and hopes about my voice, it seemed that my SFF (Speaking Fundamental Frequency) and my FRP (Frequency Range of Phonation) were just about average, but my MPT (Maximum Phonation Time) was way below. In proper English, it was even more depressing. My speech was loud but not long. The average male can keep saying 'Aaah' for 34.6 seconds. (The range for normals was 30.2 to 39.4 seconds, in case any of you were getting worried. Or boastful.) I could only manage 23.7 seconds. They were *good* seconds, mind you, but there weren't enough of them. It was a crushing blow to be told by an ex-Nearly-Miss-America that I was 10.9 seconds behind the average male. I mean, I wasn't aiming at Olympic medal standards, but even so, to be 10.9 seconds behind the *average* was a bitter pill to swallow. It took me some time to regain my composure; actually it took 4.06 seconds to recover. (I believe the average for males recovering from a similar blow to their ego is 9.45 seconds, so at least I was ahead there.) Of course, I had a reason for doing so badly on this test. Eight years ago I had a rare muscle disease which left me with wasted chest muscles and some difficulties in the breathing and singing department. Linda agreed that this would explain my poor performance (although she might have been trying to be polite), and I offered to show her a letter from my doctor if she didn't believe me. She graciously declined, and we moved on to Round Two.

In this game, I had to sing the lowest note I could manage and slide upwards to the highest. It's pretty embarrassing doing that sort of thing in front of a Miss America nominee, but I had a stab at it. She pressed a few more buttons and promptly analysed my musical range (known as the FRP in the trade). It turned out to be 34 semitones in total, going from 79 Hz to 543 Hz. I wasn't absolutely sure I knew what a Hz was. (I thought it was a car hire firm, actually, but I didn't want to say so in case I sounded stupid – as well as loud but not long), but if the numbers were all right I wasn't going to bother her. In essence, my frequency range meant that I was a normal male in singing range but not quite a Frank Sinatra. This came as a great relief to me, since although Sinatra is immensely wealthy and famous, he doesn't have as much hair as I do (one of the few ways in which people can tell us apart), and I've always suspected that it's his singing that has made him bald. So once *that* was settled we moved on again.

Round Three was designed to find out my Jitter Ratio. I can't quite remember how Linda measured my Jitter Ratio (and if you can think of a way, you're probably wrong), but it turned out to be 4.6 per cent. Personally, I thought that a Jitter Ratio of 4.6 per cent was pretty bloody magnificent for an English doctor doing silly things in front of a Miss Almost America after being told that he's 10.9 seconds short in the MPT, but Linda disagreed. According to her, 4.6 per cent was just about average. I suppose, given the nerve-wracking circumstances, that means that I have a relatively jitter-proof voice – which could be a major asset on certain occasions. For instance, one might wish to say certain phrases during which it is very important not to be nervous or jittery even if the words aren't exactly true, e.g. 'I have nothing to declare, officer' or 'Read my lips, no new taxes', etc. Perhaps the people that really succeed in this world (or America anyway) are the ones with the lowest Jitter Ratios. This might explain a great deal.

Round Four was the reading test. Now, I knew I wouldn't have any problems there because the only prize I ever won at my school in twelve years was the Reading Prize. However, I wasn't quite prepared for how dull a reading piece could be. 'Marvin Williams is only nine. Marvin lives with his mother in Monroe Avenue. Marvin loves all the movies, even eerie ones with evil villains in them.' To be honest, I got a little bored with Marvin Williams, whose life seemed to be the epitome of Backstreet USA. So I created a little more excitement in the daily routine of the Williams family, and made it up as I read it. 'Marvin Williams goes to the cinema with his mother. Marvin Williams doesn't know that his mother is an axe murderer. Marvin Williams goes to school every day. Marvin Williams enjoys mathematics, geography, recreational drugs, setting fire to public buildings and dressing in women's clothes. Marvin Williams has a lot of friends and a very smart lawyer. Marvin Williams will be eligible for parole in 1992, so look out America!' Linda, unlike any other Miss America nominee I have ever met, had a wonderful sense of humour and laughed continuously. Unfortunately her electronic gadgetry could measure Glottal Efficiency and Mean Flow Rate, but not Creative Rewriting of Test Pieces or even Potential Slander of Marvin Williams and His Mother. As a result, although I had shown myself to have a bizarre turn of mind, I had not spent enough time enunciating the sounds 's', 'a' and 'z' (although 'axe murderer' had a few) and so I scored only 87.8 per cent of the Voice/Voiceless segment test. It was another major disappointment for me and Linda, but a moral victory for Marvin Williams and his silver-haired psychopathic mother.

The phonation tests were now complete, and Linda had enough hard data on my voice characteristics to discourage me from ever trying to make anonymous phone calls. She delivered me back to the energetic and enthusiastic Dr Robert Sataloff, whose face was now wearing the Smile on the Face of the Tiger. He took me into another little cubby-hole filled with another wallfull of electronics, only this time it looked a little more serious. This time there was something that looked like a dentist's chair and a whole variety of shiny instruments that looked a lot like something Laurence Olivier would have used in *Marathon Man*. I must say that Dr Sataloff was wonderfully efficient and put me at my ease instantly – despite the fact that the film crew were clearly settling in to enjoy themselves, which always means that they know something I don't. He produced a little throat spray of local anaesthetic, tilted my head back and squirted a couple of doses down my throat and up my nose. It was, I imagine, a little bit like being hit with the anti-personnel gas called 'mace'. I burst into a fit of coughing and sneezing, but then a few seconds later my nasal passages and pharynx went completely numb. Sataloff explained that he would be using an instrument called a fibre-optic laryngoscope, which is basically a tiny thin flexible periscope that can be poked into a person's nose and down the back of their throat, and through which their vocal cords can be seen and televised through a camera at the top end.

Funnily enough, the only thought that bothered me was to do with the first bit. It occurred to me that in a couple of minutes the entire television-watching world would be seeing the inside of my nose, and I wondered if there was anything there that shouldn't be there. I mean, like most normal people I have a quick glance in the mirror every morning to check for any untoward objects in the nostrils, ears or moustache, but I don't normally do a full exploration of the major orifices on the off chance that somebody is going to burrow up my nose and halfway into my brain with a TV camera. It occurred to me that all kinds of things might be up there. As well as the expected stalactites, there might be the yellow Lego brick which my youngest daughter pushed into my face six years ago and which I have never seen since. There might be any number of peanuts which have disappeared during cocktail parties and which definitely never made it to the swallowing stage. There might be several missing shirt buttons, wife's ear-rings, aspirins or any of the hundreds of tiny domestic objects which have gone missing when in the vicinity of the human face's very own Bermuda Triangle. Fortunately, all was clear, and the laryngoscope negotiated the upper reaches of my nostrils without encountering, as it were, any skeletons in my nasal cupboard.

Dr Sataloff manoeuvred the thin tube down the back of my nose and painlessly pushed it down my anaesthetised throat. What happened next disoriented me totally. Sataloff turned on the television camera and fed the image to a large screen so that the film crew could film it – and I could see it. I was looking down my own throat. At first I couldn't see anything except a foamy white appearance that could easily have been a scenic shot of the sea at Beachy Head. This was, according to Sataloff, the normal pool of saliva lurking just above my vocal cords (I hope you're not reading this while having tea). He asked me to swallow. I did so, and on the screen the waves of the salivary Red Sea parted, and

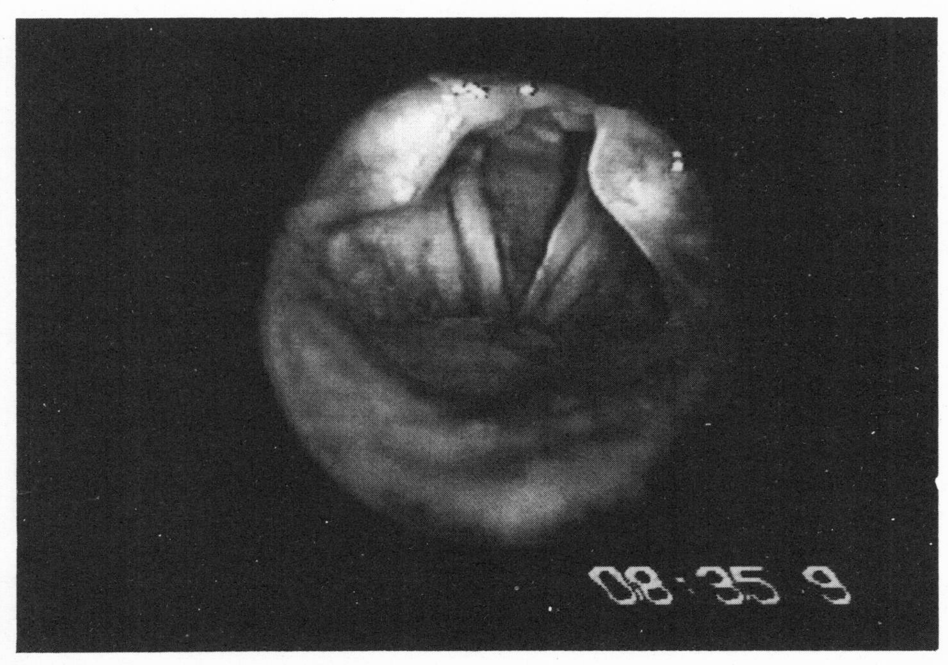

Portrait of the artist as a laryngoscopist's subject
The author's vocal cords do their award-winning imitation of an extra-terrestrial parrot from *Aliens*.

through the foam I could see my own vocal cords. They appeared to wink at me. For a bizarre moment I had the impression that they could see out as clearly as I could see in. This was a very crazy thought, and I told myself to get a grip on reality. In fact, my vocal cords looked utterly disgusting. I have seen lots of other people's vocal cords (since I did several stints in emergency medicine during which I became quite handy with a laryngoscope myself) but I had never seen them, as it were, working. Mine looked to me like a beaky animal from *Aliens*, or perhaps like a sparrow with half of its head missing.

Most of the television screen was filled with a lurid pink mass (my epiglottis and some things called the valeculae), in the centre of which there appeared to be a diamond-shaped beak. I spoke a few words, and as I did so the little beak opened and closed, giving the uncanny impression of a bizarre and perverted ventriloquist act. As I said, 'Hello, my name is Robert Buckman', the beak seemed to be mouthing along with my words, following them with uncanny timing. It took a moment for me to think through the reality of the situation. In fact, my vocal cords were making the sounds that I was hearing as 'Hello', etc. However, we are all so accustomed to seeing a face doing the talking that we think human speech comes from mouths and lips, and forget that the sound actually originates lower down in the larynx. In some respects, the vocal cords really do their very own ventriloquist's act – they create the noises and make us think that the lips are doing the talking. I was now peeking behind the scenes. It was most odd.

Dr Sataloff was clearly very pleased with what was going on and ran my vocal cords through a complete range of tests, which they passed with flying colours. Then came Dunstan's little surprise. Dr Sataloff removed the laryngoscope from my nose (with no Lego bricks or peanuts stuck to the end of it) and surreptitiously picked up a larger instrument from the equipment table. I had a quick glimpse of it before he swung into action. To me, it looked like a small gleaming pneumatic drill. It had a chunky sort of stock and a stubby stainless-steel spike sticking out of the end which was about twelve inches long and about half an inch in diameter. It was clear that Dr Sataloff was going to ram this spike down my throat. It was equally clear (to me) that it would come straight out of the back of my neck, taking with it several important parts of my lower brain and producing a state that in medical parlance is called 'death'. Out of the corner of my eye, I could see Dunstan winking at Dr Sataloff and I tried to say something but found that I couldn't speak. This was because Dr Sataloff had got hold of my tongue in a piece of gauze and was pulling it out of my mouth. Actually, this was the worst bit of the whole thing. I don't mind sticking my tongue out, I don't even mind holding it (literally or metaphorically), but it is quite a different matter when somebody else does the holding. The feeling of terror and loss of control is totally unnerving.

Dr Sataloff told me to say 'Aaah'. I don't think I really said it, I bellowed it. And while I did so he rammed the stainless steel spike in. To my surprise, my brain was not pushed out of the back of my head. In fact, all that happened was that a slightly different view of my vocal cords came up on the screen and distracted me from my bellowing terror. The gleaming machine was actually a stroboscopic laryngoscope which allows doctors to watch their victim's vocal cords in slow motion. On the screen, my voice box now looked blue and then started flickering like an empty and rather gloomy disco. Apparently, this was just what Dr Sataloff wanted to see, and he enthusiastically demonstrated how my right vocal cord developed a slightly irregular flutter at certain frequencies. However, he assured me, I need not worry about this unless I was contemplating singing in Wagnerian opera. With a foot of stainless-steel spike down my throat and the film crew doubled up with laughter, I nodded vigorously to assure Dr Sataloff that that was the last thing on my mind. With professional help, he told me, my right vocal cord flutter could be fixed, and my singing could be improved. The way I felt that instant, my instinct was to tell him that if the treatment involved any more sessions with the steel spike, I could quite happily spend the rest of my professional career as a mime artiste. But I didn't actually tell him, mostly because he was still holding my tongue.

And then it was over. My professional voice had received its care and was clearly afflicted with a few deficiencies. I hadn't done as well as I had hoped, but on the other hand I hadn't done quite as badly as I had feared. I was obviously no Pavarotti. On the other hand, Pavarotti was probably no doctor. I took comfort in the thought that I could probably do a better job of singing *Tannhäuser* than Pavarotti could of doing my medical out-patients clinic. Let's hope that neither of us ever have to find out.

11
CONCLUSION:
What America Is All About

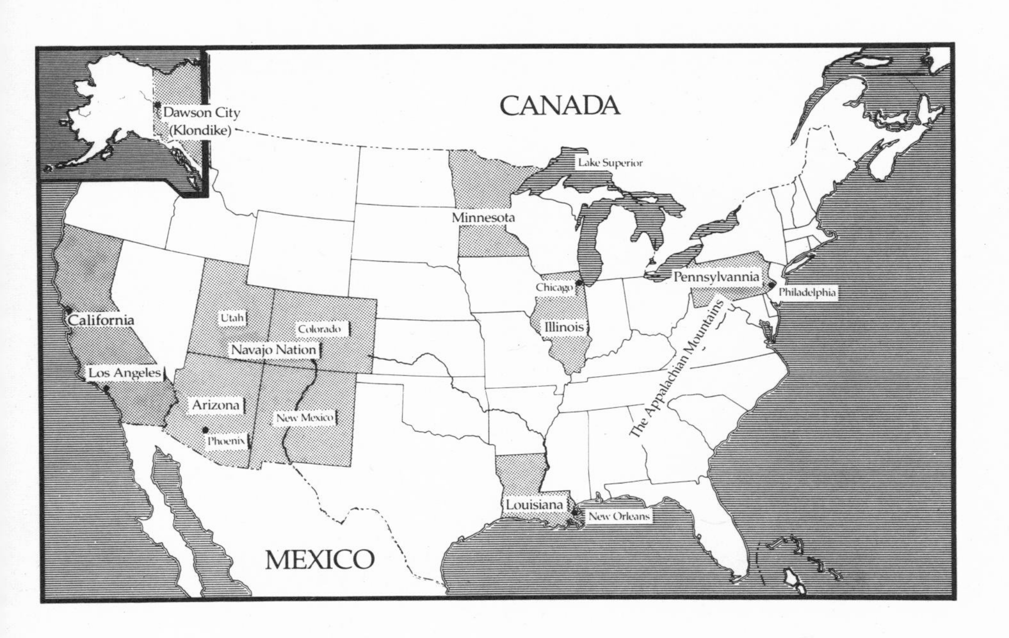

Often during our excursions, I found myself shaking my head slowly at America and the Americans, frequently in amazement, sometimes in admiration, occasionally in awe and sporadically in dismay. America seems to me to be like a much-admired and much-loved hyperactive younger cousin – someone who is perhaps brilliantly talented, who writes better poems or paints better paintings than anyone else in the world, but who also has lapses of bad behaviour, picks his nose at table, tears the wings off butterflies and makes rude faces at old ladies.

America contains more creative energy than anywhere in the world, but it suffers from two major vices which detract from its potential: profligacy and selfishness. Of the first, and of the way America wilfully wastes its natural resources (and everybody else's), I can't really give an authoritative analysis. My command of economics is so poor that I get migraine thinking about anything more complex than a discount for cash. But the other vice – the selfishness, the dark side of free enterprise, the 'I'm all right, Jack' – comes through loud and clear when you listen to what the patients and their doctors have to say.

Of course, I am not an economist or a sociologist, I am a doctor. Furthermore, I am a doctor who was born in a country which at that moment had decided that every citizen had the right to a health service. I grew up with the National Health Service (literally and metaphorically) and I never knew a Britain without it. For me, it is a fixed pillar of the British view of the world; it has always been that way and (I hope) it will always remain so. In America, the opposite applies. There is no National Health Service and there (probably) never will be. They regard our medicine (correctly) as 'socialised'; but in a country where 'liberal' is now used as an insult and 'socialist' is almost an expletive, the word 'socialised' condemns it for ever.

Emergency care is available for those who are dangerously ill and poor, but if you need some less urgent care and you can't afford it, forget it. Even for the middle class, a chronic illness can be a financial wipe-out. In many cases, medical insurance goes with the job. So if you lose your job (a recognised precipitant of some kinds of illness) you may lose your medical insurance at the same time. The writer Joseph Heller calculated the cost of his recent – and temporary – muscle disease at $100,000 (around £60,000). Being a best-selling author, he could afford it, but what if the patient had not been good old Joe Heller but poor old Joe Soap, what then? What if Peter had not caught the wolf?

The central problem is the phrase 'equality of opportunity'. The equal opportunity of following one's own 'life, liberty and the pursuit of happiness' has one or two biological limitations. Let's face it, human beings are not created *physically* equal. Some are tall, some are short, some are strong, some are weak, some have the constitutions of an ox and can be dropped from the third storey of a building without damaging anything except the pavement, and some are born to be 94-pound weaklings or invalids. That's the way it is with all biological species (of which humans, no matter what we pretend, are one). We may choose to do something about that (by treating the weak and the ill, and helping them to keep up with the healthy) or we may choose to ignore it and pretend it doesn't exist. And may the devil take the hindmost, survival of the fittest, nature is red in tooth and claw, bad luck, excuse me, I've got other things to do.

Certainly, every American citizen has the theoretical opportunity of becoming President. The President might emerge from an impoverished background – as the ex-rail-splitter Abraham Lincoln did – although probably that will never happen again. Or he (or even she) might be a descendant of a glittering lineage of distinguished aristocrats as Jack Kennedy was. But you can never be President if you die before adulthood due to lack of medical care. For instance, none of the 30 per cent of babies born to Chicago's black schoolgirl mothers, who die before their first birthday, are going to get a chance at anything. And that's the problem; you can only join the equal scramble for opportunity if you're alive and (reasonably) well. So if you happen to be born (or to become) sickly and you can't afford medical care, you won't get the opportunity of enjoying the promised equality of opportunity. And that sticks in my throat.

I'm not claiming that the British system is perfect, because it isn't. There are considerable inequalities of health in Britain (Professor Sir Douglas Black's book of that very title has a full analysis). If you have an illness, you're likely to do better if you live in the South-East than if you suffer from the same illness in the North-West. But the point is that the British are committed to *trying* to offer equal health to all (even if they don't succeed all the time), and the Americans are committed to offering health to the rich and/or insured (even if the poor get the occasional look-in from services like the paramedics and medicare). I suppose it all revolves around what you consider the word 'freedom' really means. To me it means an absence of things that restrict you – and in my view, illness is one of those things. In the American view, it isn't, and you don't have the right to become ill and complain if you can't afford treatment.

I don't really understand why America's idea of freedom entails, as a fundamental principle, the right to carry guns but not the right to get medical treatment. I'm not sure why they believe that the freedom to carry handguns which are designed to maim and kill other citizens is an inalienable right, whereas the freedom to stay alive among the same citizens is the prerogative of those who can afford it.

To this National-Health-trained doctor, the United States is a maddening and contradictory continent, bursting with creative inventiveness, brilliance and promise, but hampered with a lack of concern for its own people which makes it, at the same time, a paradise for the lucky and a hell for the unlucky. Perhaps my own feeling about the States can be summed up in what the Americans always used to say of Britain in the seventies: 'A nice place to visit, but I wouldn't want to live there.' I shall *definitely* be back for more visits next year. America is not now, has never been and never will be dull.

I refuse to say more on the grounds that it might incriminate me.

Picture Acknowledgements

The photographs are reproduced by courtesy of Jeff Alexander, Elizabeth Barrett, Paul Dunstan, Charles Flynn, Greg Guirard, Mostafa Hammuri, Adam Hart-Davis, Marc Pokempner, and the author's private collection.